THE DIABETES
DTOUR DIET
JOURNAL

Workout Photos by Jonathan Pozniak; Styling by Marie Bloomquist and Hair and Makeup by Lynn Lamorte, both for Vivian Artists

Book design by Jill Armus

Library of Congress Cataloging-in-Publication Data is on file with the publisher.

ISBN-13 978-1-60529-583-1
ISBN-10 1-60529-583-3

2 4 6 8 10 9 7 5 3 1 paperback

RODALE
LIVE YOUR WHOLE LIFE™

We inspire and enable people to improve their lives and the world around them
For more of our products visit **rodalestore.com** or call 800-848-4735

THE
DIABETES
DTOUR
DIET
JOURNAL

YOUR PORTABLE PLANNER
FOR WEIGHT-LOSS SUCCESS

BARBARA QUINN, MS, RD, CDE,
AND THE EDITORS OF
Prevention.
with Medical Advisor
Francine R. Kaufman, MD

RODALE

INTRODUCTION

Welcome to the DTOUR Diet Journal—or as we like to call it, DTOUR to go!

We know how challenging sticking with an eating plan, or any kind of plan, can be. All of us have the best of intentions, but somehow life usually manages to throw us a curve or two. Like those days when your lunch hour turns into a lunch 10 minutes, and your only options are the break-room vending machine and your co-worker's candy dish. Or you're so upset by a spat with your spouse that every bone in your body wants to tear into a package of Oreos.

In moments like these, a little on-the-spot motivation and inspiration can help you navigate the dietary minefields and keep you on the path to success. That's what the DTOUR Diet Journal can do for you, and more!

We've distilled the most important information and tools from DTOUR into a user-friendly portable format, so you have it at your fingertips whenever you need it. You'll find all of the journal pages here, including the daily menus for the 2-Week Fast Start as well as the mix-and-match meals and snacks for the 4-Week Total Transformation. Use these to prepare for the day ahead or to guide your food choices when you're on the go. It makes eating healthfully a whole lot easier.

The journal also features the complete DTOUR Workout, plus lots of tips for managing stress and getting a good night's sleep. All of these are important not just for losing weight but for controlling your blood sugar, too.

At the end of the journal, you'll find extra pages that you can use to stay on DTOUR until you reach your goal weight—or to help maintain your weight once you get there. Studies have shown that keeping a journal is one of the most effective weight-loss tools around. It's especially helpful for tracking your eating habits and troubleshooting situations when you may be taking in more calories than you realize.

On DTOUR, of course, we've already counted all the calories for you. All you need to do is choose the right calorie level for you: 1,400 if you're a woman who's small in stature or your fairly sedentary; 1,600 if you're a woman who's tall or very active or you're a man. Then follow the appropriate plan to the letter, and you'll be getting just the right mix of macronutrients (carbohydrate, protein, and fat), plus generous daily dosages of our fabulous Fat-Fighting 4 supernutrients (fiber, calcium, vitamin D, and omega-3s). That's the DTOUR recipe for success!

On this plan, you can see results rather quickly; our DTOUR test panelists lost up to 13 pounds through the 2-Week Fast Start, and up to 25 pounds over the full 6 weeks. Their blood sugar stabilized or dropped significantly, too. But we want to be clear: DTOUR isn't about a quick fix. It's about learning a way of eating—and a way of living—that's going to keep you fit, healthy, and energized for years to come. That's just as good as the changes you'll see in the mirror.

—The Editors of *Prevention*

P.S.—Don't forget that you can find all the DTOUR menus, recipes, and lifestyle tools online at www.dtour.com. Check it out!

THE DTOUR FAT-FIGHTING 4

The Diabetes DTOUR Diet is based on exciting new science that focuses on the Fat-Fighting 4: four superstar nutrients that combine to help lower blood sugar and melt away pounds. This truly awesome foursome—fiber, calcium, vitamin D, and omega-3s—is the key to good health. And all are in plentiful supply in DTOUR!

Fat Fighter #1: Fiber—Fill Up to Slim Down

A half century of research has proven fiber to be the Swiss Army knife of nutrients. Name just about any health problem and a high-fiber diet probably can help treat it, if not prevent it in the first place.

Trying to lose weight? Then fiber-rich foods definitely are the way to go. Case in point: Researchers at the University of Minnesota found that people who ate the most vegetables, fruits, and other fiber-rich foods lost 2 to 3 pounds more per month than those on lower-fiber diets.

With all the good things it has going for it, fiber ought to be a dietary mainstay. Yet a full two-thirds of us are getting 15 grams a day, at most. That's about half of the recommended 25 to 30 grams a day!

Why are so many of us coming up so short? The answer, at least in part, is that fiber-rich whole foods must compete with processed foods for our dietary favor. The latter's very name suggests their inherent weakness: Processed foods are pretty much devoid of fiber.

DTOUR is all about whole foods—fruits, veggies, beans, and whole grains. They're the staple ingredients of our menus and recipes, which are as easy to make as they are fabulous to eat! You'll enjoy stir-fries, bean tostadas, pasta primavera, and pancakes—yes, pancakes!—on this diet. And no worries about fiber: You'll be getting between 26 and 29 grams every day, depeding on your calorie level. You'll eat great, lose weight, and rein in your blood sugar. That's the DTOUR promise!

THE 411 ON FIBER

So just what is fiber? Simply put, it's the component of a plant food that passes through the digestive system pretty much intact. The term *fiber* actually describes a group of plant compounds, each with different functions and health benefits and each generally categorized as soluble or insoluble.

Soluble fiber is the kind that dissolves in water and turns into a thick gel during digestion. The humble apple, which contains a modest 80 calories but an impressive 5 grams of fiber, is an excellent source of a particular soluble fiber called pectin. If the name rings a bell, it's because pectin is used as a thickener in foods like jams and jellies. The same properties allow

PEANUT BUTTER: FIBER-FULL INDULGENCE

On the Diabetes DTOUR Diet, a "weakness" for peanut butter works to your advantage. That's because when it comes to weight loss and blood sugar control, PB is A-OK. Here's why.

It helps you lose weight. Yes, PB packs 180 to 210 calories per serving. But its winning combo of fiber and protein—2 grams and 8 grams per serving, respectively—fills you up and keeps you feeling full longer, so you eat less overall. Plus, there's nothing more indulgent than licking peanut butter off a spoon—and indulgence (in moderation) helps dieters master cravings and stay on track.

It's a diabetes foe. Peanuts can reduce your risk of diabetes and heart disease. A 2002 study published in the *Journal of the American Medical Association* found that consuming 1 ounce of nuts or peanut butter (about 2 tablespoons) at least 5 days a week can lower the risk of diabetes by almost 30 percent.

It's packed with belly-flattening fat. Peanut butter is rich in heart-healthy monounsaturated fat. In one study, people with insulin resistance who ate a diet high in monos had less belly fat than people who ate more carbohydrates or saturated fat.

The fat and calorie counts of most brands of peanut butter are similar, but there are other indicators of a healthy pick. Here's what to look for.

◆ **Sodium:** Counts can range from 40 to 250 milligrams per 2-tablespoon serving. Organic versions tend to have less.

◆ **Sugar:** Natural brands have 1 to 2 grams, about half as much as commercial brands.

PS: No need to select reduced-fat PB. It contains about the same number of calories as full-fat brands, if not more—thanks to ingredients intended to make up for the missing fat, such as added sugar.

pectin to "thicken" in your digestive tract. The result: You feel fuller after eating.

Soluble fiber's gummy texture also may interfere with carbohydrate and glucose absorption in the intestines, leading to lower blood sugar and insulin. With your blood sugar on an even keel, you're better able to manage hunger and cravings.

Another benefit of soluble fiber is its ability to lower cholesterol. One study found that for every gram of soluble fiber consumed in a diet of primarily fruits, veggies, and whole grains, blood cholesterol could decline by as much as 2 percent.

Unlike soluble fiber, insoluble fiber—your grandmother called it roughage—doesn't dissolve in water. Because it stays solid, it adds bulk to bowel movements. It also speeds the passage of food through the digestive tract, which means the intestines have less time to absorb carbohydrates. The result: Your blood sugar stays on an even keel.

Among the best sources of insoluble fiber are whole wheat flour, wheat bran, and many vegetables; for soluble fiber, top-notch sources include oats, peas, beans, apples, and citrus fruits. That said, plant foods vary greatly in the types and amounts of fiber they contain. Your best bet is to vary your food choices—which is exactly what you'll be doing on DTOUR!

EASY WAYS TO GET YOUR FIBER FILL

You're going to be getting a lot of fiber on DTOUR, perhaps more than you're accustomed to eating. So we've put together a list of tips for you to follow now, before you start the plan. Don't try them all at once; your digestive tract may not forgive you. Instead, choose one or two that seem doable to you. By the way, these same strategies guided us in developing the DTOUR menus and recipes. So think of them as a head start!

◆ Select a breakfast cereal that provides 5 or more grams of fiber per serving. Another option: Add 2 tablespoons of unprocessed wheat bran to your favorite nonsugary cereal.

◆ Switch to a whole grain bread that contains at least 2 grams of fiber per serving. Read labels to make sure you're getting the real thing. You should see whole wheat, whole wheat flour, or another whole grain in the top spot on the ingredient list.

◆ Eat fruit at every meal. Berries, along with pears, apples, and oranges, are good sources of fiber.

◆ Swap meat for legumes two or three times per week. Black beans, chickpeas, and edamame (whole soybeans) are high in fiber, low in fat, and packed with lean protein. Toss them in salads, or add them to chili or soups.

◆ Visit your local natural-foods store and experiment with some of the more exotic whole grains, such as buckwheat, millet, barley, and quinoa.

◆ Take advantage of ready-to-use vegetables. Mix chopped frozen broccoli into prepared spaghetti sauce, or nibble on baby carrots.

◆ Add some roughage to your snacks. Fresh fruits, raw vegetables with fat-free dip, and low-fat popcorn are all good choices.

◆ Experiment with Indian and Middle Eastern cuisines, which feature whole grains and legumes as part of the main meal. You might whip up Indian dal or Middle Eastern tabbouleh—a cracked-wheat salad flavored with lemon, fresh parsley, mint, chopped tomatoes, and spices.

SOURCES OF SOLUBLE AND INSOLUBLE FIBER

On DTOUR, you'll be getting a healthy mix of both types of fiber from top-notch sources like these.

Soluble Fiber
◆ Apples
◆ Beans and legumes
◆ Berries (blueberries, strawberries)
◆ Nuts and seeds
◆ Oatmeal and oat bran
◆ Pears

Insoluble Fiber
◆ Barley
◆ Brown rice
◆ Bulgur
◆ Carrots
◆ Celery
◆ Tomatoes
◆ Wheat bran
◆ Whole grain breads and breakfast cereals
◆ Zucchini

♦ Add ½ cup of chickpeas, either cooked or canned, to a pot of your favorite soup. You'll boost its total fiber count by 6 grams. Be sure to rinse canned chickpeas to reduce their sodium content.

♦ Steam your broccoli, cauliflower, and carrots before eating them, and you'll get 3 to 5 grams of fiber per serving—up to twice the amount in the raw veggies. Heat makes fiber more available.

♦ Use uncooked oatmeal instead of bread crumbs in meat loaf. Add ¾ cup of oats per pound of lean ground beef, and you'll boost the total fiber count to more than 8 grams.

♦ Top your fat-free ice cream with sliced fresh berries. One-half cup of raspberries provides 4 grams of fiber; the same amount of strawberries or blueberries packs 2 grams.

Fat Fighter #2: Calcium

Around the time you were learning about the basic four food groups in elementary school, you probably got a lesson or two about how milk—and, more precisely, the calcium in milk—helps build your bones. In fact, about 99 percent of the calcium in your body resides in your bones and teeth. The remaining 1 percent has a lot going on, too—helping your heart to beat, your blood to clot, and your nerves to communicate with each other. As you can see, your body needs calcium to thrive.

It's only fairly recently that researchers began to suspect a connection between calcium and weight loss. In 2002, a research team at the University of Tennessee put 32 people—all overweight—on calorie-restricted diets that included varying amounts of dietary calcium. Over the 6 months of the study, the people who ate three servings of dairy (including low-fat milk, cheese, and yogurt) lost 70 percent more weight—an average of 24 pounds— and 64 percent more body fat than those who ate just one serving a day.

Understandably, this study made national headlines. Ever since, experts have been debating the role of calcium—mainly from dairy foods—in weight loss. Now, common sense will tell you that you can't expect to slim down by eating a pint of Ben & Jerry's every day. (We know—we're disappointed, too!) On the other hand, if you make a point of stocking your daily diet with low-fat, calcium-rich choices—as you'll be doing on DTOUR—you will stack the weight-loss odds in your favor. (PS: The DTOUR Diet leaves room for ice cream, too!)

Considering all the fabulous foods that double as outstanding calcium sources, it's hard to fathom that we're not getting enough of the mineral in our daily diets. Yet many of us are missing the mark. According to a 2008 study, only 40 percent of American women between ages 20 and 49 are at or above the recommended intake of 1,000 milligrams of calcium a day; among women over 50, just 27 percent are getting the recommended 1,500 milligrams a day. (Calcium levels are of particular concern for women, because they're much more likely than men to develop osteoporosis.)

Your body has two ways of meeting its calcium needs. One is by metabolizing the mineral from calcium-rich foods and supplements, which is by far the healthiest option. The other is by absorbing it from bones, which is what happens when your blood level of calcium falls too low.

When you don't have enough calcium in your bloodstream, small glands called the parathyroids (so named because they sit on the surface of the thyroid) trigger the release of calcitriol. Calcitriol, in turn, encourages the release of calcium by breaking down bone. It also increases the kidneys' ability to reabsorb calcium, so you lose less in urine.

The solution, of course, is to keep blood calcium at a healthy level. Then calcitriol won't rise, fat cells won't hoard fat, and blood pressure will remain normal. The best way to meet your body's calcium needs is with food—and the Diabetes DTOUR Diet is chock-full of yummy, calcium-rich choices!

Fat Fighter #3: Vitamin D

We can't really talk about calcium without bringing vitamin D into the conversation, since D's most important function is to help the intestines absorb calcium. At the risk of stating the obvious, if your gut can't absorb calcium, your body can't use it.

As you'll see a bit later, calcium and vitamin D appear to work together to help fight type 2 diabetes. But vitamin D has benefits in its own right: It has shown promise in helping to protect against heart disease, as well as certain cancers and autoimmune diseases. Since the risk of heart disease rises in the presence of diabetes, we'll spend just a few moments on vitamin D's cardiovascular benefits.

To start, vitamin D plays a fundamental role in the heart's ability to pump blood and in the structure of heart cells. It also may turn down chronic inflammation, which a growing body of research is implicating as a key risk factor for heart disease.

For a recent study, Harvard researchers tracked more than 1,700 men and women for 5 years to determine if low blood levels of vitamin D led to heart disease. None of the participants had heart disease at the study's start, but 28 percent were running low on vitamin D. Those in the D-deficient group were 60 percent more likely to develop heart disease than those who had enough D.

Since this was just an observational study, the researchers can't say for sure why vitamin D appeared to have heart-protective effects. Whatever the mechanism, though, the findings advance the case for satisfying your body's vitamin D requirements.

Just as with calcium, many of us—an estimated 60 percent of Americans—aren't getting enough vitamin D, according to a survey by the Centers for Disease Control and Prevention. If we're low on vitamin D, then our shortfall of calcium makes sense. As we said earlier, our bodies can't use calcium without D. People who are deficient in vitamin D typically absorb just 10 to 15 percent of their dietary calcium, compared with 30 to 40 percent for people who are meeting their D needs.

If you're over age 50 or African American, or if you're vegan or lactose intolerant, you're more likely to experience a D deficiency than the general population. Overweight may be a risk factor, too. Though the body stores vitamin D in fat and releases it into the bloodstream on an as-needed basis, this process doesn't go quite so smoothly in the presence of extra pounds. Instead, excess body fat seems to act as a sort of trap, preventing vitamin D from entering the bloodstream.

One other possible explanation for our national D deficit: sunscreen. You see, the human body synthesizes its own vitamin D when exposed to the sun's ultraviolet rays. Though it's highly controversial, a growing number of experts believe that since we've become so indoctrinated in the use of sunscreen, we don't give sunlight a chance to penetrate our well-protected hides. In effect, we're setting ourselves up for deficiency.

Our bodies need all the vitamin D they can get, whether it comes from sunlight (about 10 minutes a day of unprotected exposure), from food, or from supplements—or, ideally, a combination of the three.

GETTING THE CALCIUM AND D YOU NEED

When you consider all that calcium and vitamin D can do for your body, you have plenty of good reasons to make sure you're getting enough of both nutrients. Never fear: The Diabetes DTOUR Diet covers your nutritional bases, and then some! Our menus and recipes deliver 1,200 milligrams of calcium and 155 IU of vitamin D, on average, every day. These levels, in combination with a vitamin D supplement, meet or beat the government guidelines for most people. (They are lower than the amounts some experts are recommending for therapeutic purposes, but the jury is still out on just how much calcium and vitamin D is necessary and safe.)

Our diet does feature a variety of dairy foods and dairy-based dishes, since dairy is just about the best dietary source of calcium around. Just three glasses of fortified fat-free milk offers more than 1,000 milligrams of calcium, plus 400 IU of vitamin D. But what if you can't do dairy because you're lactose intolerant? One option is to use lactose-free or soy-based products; the fortified varieties are just as nutritious as the "real thing," and they taste great, too! You also might try using Lactaid or another supplement that contains lactase, an enzyme that helps your body digest lactose. You can get significant amounts of calcium from nondairy sources like fortified tofu; canned salmon and sardines (with their bones); and dark green, leafy vegetables. See the chart on page 14 highlights your best choices.

As for vitamin D, if the latest research is any indication, even current government guidelines—which range from 200 IU to 600 IU, based on age—may be falling short. How much higher they ought to be is the subject of considerable debate. Based on what we know so far, we think it makes good sense for everyone to take supplemental vitamin D.

How much do you need in supplement form? If you're age 70 or younger, 400 IU a day—in combination with the DTOUR menus and recipes—will cover your body's needs and then some. If you're 71 or older, your goal is a bit higher—600 IU a day. That's because your body may not be synthesizing its own D as efficiently.

You also might consider taking extra calcium and vitamin D as nutritional insurance—if, for example, you spend a lot of your time indoors (which means your skin may not be synthesizing vitamin D) or you're at risk of osteoporosis. Your doctor can help you decide whether you require more than the recommended amounts of these nutrients.

FOOD SOURCES OF CALCIUM

From fish to beans to greens, calcium crops up in a wide variety of tasty foods.

FOOD	AMOUNT	CALCIUM (MG) PER SERVING
Soy milk, fortified	1 c	368
Sardines, oil-packed, drained	3 oz	325
Tofu, firm, prepared with nigari (a natural solidifier)	½ c	253
Salmon, canned, with bone	3 oz	181
Collards, cooked	½ c	178
Molasses, blackstrap	1 Tbsp	172
Spinach, cooked	½ c	146
Oatmeal, fortified, instant	1 packet	99-110
White beans, canned	½ c	96
Kale, cooked	½ c	90

FOOD SOURCES OF VITAMIN D

Fish and fortified foods are excellent sources of vitamin D.

FOOD	AMOUNT	VITAMIN D (IU) PER SERVING
Salmon, cooked	3½ oz	360
Mackerel, cooked	3½ oz	345
Sardines, oil-packed, drained	1¾ oz	250
Tuna, oil-packed, drained	3 oz	200
Quaker Nutrition for Women Instant Oatmeal	1 packet	154
Soy milk, fortified	1 c	100
Milk, fortified, fat-free, low-fat, or whole	1 c	98
Cereal, fortified	¾-1 c	40-50

Fat Fighter #4:
Omega-3s—Good for Your
Heart—And Your Waistline

Most experts agree that the right fats, in the right amounts, can be—make that *should* be—part of a healthy diet. By the right fats we mean omega-3 fatty acids, the kind that help melt away pounds and lower heart disease risk (which tends to be higher in those with blood sugar issues). These fats also may improve cells' insulin response!

Virtually every meal and snack in DTOUR delivers a delicious dose of omega-3s. Depending on which calorie level of our diet is best for you, you'll be getting between 2.5 and 2.7 grams over the course of a day. That's well above the recommended 1.1 grams for women and 1.6 grams for men.

DTOUR derives its omega-3s from a variety of foods, including fish, walnuts, and flaxseed. Of these, cold-water fish, such as salmon, albacore tuna, and sardines, are by far the most abundant sources of the two types of omega-3s: eicosapentaenoic acid (EPA) and docosahexaenoic acid (DHA). (Don't worry; you're only eating them—not pronouncing them!) We've also included foods that supply alpha-linolenic acid (ALA), another kind of fatty acid that your body cleverly converts into omega-3s.

When you're getting enough omega-3s in your diet—and that's a guarantee on DTOUR—they can do some pretty amazing things for you. Some of the most exciting research currently underway is exploring the potential for omega-3s to help shrink your waistline.

Like all fats—whether good or bad—omega-3s promote satiety, the feeling of contentment at the end of a meal that signals you've eaten your fill. (That's why most of us would scale a 10-foot fence if we knew a full-fat chocolate-chip cookie was waiting on the other side.)

Omega-3s may go one better, however. The results of a 2007 study published in the *American Journal of Clinical Nutrition* suggest that omega-3s may help burn body fat, shrink abdominal fat cells, and thwart certain genes that trigger inflammation in belly fat.

Though few clinical studies have examined the direct impact of omega-3s on diabetes risk, other research offers convincing evidence for the potential benefits of these good fats for people with blood sugar issues. In particular, omega-3s may reduce insulin resistance and inflammation, raise good HDL cholesterol, lower triglycerides, and improve the function of the tissue that lines arteries. These cardiovascular effects are important, since heart disease is a common complication of diabetes.

9 Ways to Sneak In More 3s

The Diabetes DTOUR Diet is designed to satisfy your body's omega-3 needs—as well as your taste buds! Your daily dose is spread across each day's menu, so you'll get a little bit at every meal and snack.

To help ease you into the omega-3 habit, we've compiled a list of our favorite tips and techniques for taking advantage of these beneficial fats. Take them for a test-drive now, before you embark on DTOUR. They'll also serve as helpful guideposts while you're on the plan, helping you to stay the course while you're slimming down.

◆ Rebalance your dietary ratio of omega-3s to omega-6s. It's simple: As you increase your intake of omega-3-rich foods, cut way back on processed foods, refined grains, and supermarket cooking oils—the chief sources of omega-6s in the average diet.

◆ Munch a DTOUR salad every day—a potent combo of leafy greens and veggies dressed with walnut, canola, or flaxseed oil and a sprinkling of sesame seeds.

◆ Eat salmon or another type of cold-water fish two or three times a week. You'll get those beneficial omega-3s—and if the fish is replacing red meat in your diet, you'll probably be consuming less saturated fat.

◆ For lunch, help yourself to a tuna sandwich. Make your tuna with canola-oil mayo.

◆ Try tofu—really! Tofu and other products made with soybeans are good sources of omega-3s. You can always add tofu to stir-fries, but for variety, try pureeing it with peanut butter for a fluffy sandwich spread or blending soft tofu with a banana for a breakfast smoothie.

◆ Add 1½ tablespoons of ground flaxseed or 1 teaspoon of flaxseed oil to your diet every day. You can mix the seeds into low-fat cottage cheese or the oil into a smoothie.

◆ Use canola oil to cook and flaxseed oil for salad dressings. (Flaxseed oil breaks down when it's heated, so it's not good for cooking.)

◆ Eat walnuts. As nuts go, they're the only kind rich in omega-3s. They may be good for the heart, too. When researchers in Spain asked a group of volunteers to eat 8 to 13 walnuts a day in tandem with a heart-healthy diet, this group showed 64 percent stronger artery-pumping action and 20 percent fewer of the gunky molecules that lead to atherosclerotic plaque than did a control group who followed the heart-healthy diet but skipped the nuts.

◆ Consider switching to eggs enriched with omega-3s. Many producers now add sources of omega-3 fats such as flaxseed and canola oil to the hens' feed to increase the healthy fats in their eggs. Look for cartons that carry the USDA-certified label; these eggs have been inspected, so you can feel confident that their claims (such as "omega-3 enhanced") are legit.

FOOD SOURCES OF ALA

You can boost your daily intake of omega-3s by consuming more ALA, which your body converts to omega-3s. Among the best sources:

FOOD	ALA
Flaxseed oil, 1 Tbsp	6.6 g
Ground flaxseed, 2 Tbsp	3.2 g
Canola oil, 1 Tbsp	1.6 g
Walnut oil, 1 Tbsp	1.4 g
Soybeans, cooked, 1 c	1.1 g
Soybean oil, 1 Tbsp	1.0 g
Walnuts, 2 Tbsp	1.0 g
Firm tofu, ½ c	0.7 g

(HOW TO) GET ON DTOUR!

Before you jump in, we want to acquaint you with the DTOUR How-Tos. These four simple, sensible rules form the foundation of our diet. In fact, once you finish the 6 weeks of DTOUR, the How-Tos can help ensure that your weight and blood sugar level remain healthy and stable. Stick with them, and they can keep you fit and vital for years to come.

DTOUR How-To #1: Track Your Calories

Notice we didn't say *count*. If you're a numbers type and counting calories helps you stay on track, by all means carry on. On the other hand, if—like many dieters—you consider this task only slightly more tolerable than having a root canal, then DTOUR is your diet dream come true. We've already done the calculations for you; all you need to do is eat!

Just remember this: Even if you don't count calories, calories still count. And if your objective is to lose weight, you need to burn more calories than you consume. It's that simple, and we all know it instinctively. Still, we need an occasional reminder that, at the end of the day, it's how any effective diet works.

So, you do want to keep an eye on your calorie intake. But guessing at a number can be a gamble. If you're off by even 100 calories a day, you can end up gaining between 6 and 10 pounds in a year. Experts say this is one reason why women in their forties today are about 25 pounds heavier than women of the same age back in 1960.

We're all different, and so are our calorie needs, which are based on age, gender, and activity level, among other factors. In general, though, both women and men can lose as much as 2 pounds a week by limiting their calories to no more than 1,600 calories a day.

On DTOUR, you have two calorie levels to choose from: 1,400 and 1,600. If you're a relatively sedentary woman who's short in stature, the 1,400-calorie plan is about right for you. For women who are tall or physically active and for men, the 1,600-calorie plan is the better option. Just bear in mind that at the higher calorie level, you may occasionally need to dip a little lower if you want to speed up weight loss or break through a plateau.

Now, here's the best part: Once you've chosen your calorie level, DTOUR takes care of the rest! The 2-Week Fast Start is carefully structured to provide approximately the same number of calories per day, give or take a few. Once you graduate to the 4-Week Total Transformation, you get to choose your meals and snacks—but even as you mix and match, your daily calories will stay on track. How's that for easy?

DTOUR How-To #2: Practice Portion Control, Seriously!

Though you don't need to count calories on DTOUR, you will need to pay attention to your portion sizes. Different portion sizes of the same foods determine your calorie intake—and, frankly, they're often responsible for thwarting the best-laid weight-loss plans.

Before you begin DTOUR, you'll want to make sure that you have the following equipment on hand: measuring cups, a food scale, and a set of measuring spoons. In practice, it takes mere moments to weigh and measure your food. Those few seconds can determine whether you'll be slipping into your skinny jeans or squeezing into a bigger size.

At home, it's easy to practice portion control. Keep your measuring tools right on your kitchen counter and use them to measure the ingredients in your meals and snacks, as well as the actual serving sizes. Place the correct portion on your plate and leave the serving dishes on the counter. That way, you'll think twice before helping yourself to seconds!

Monitoring portions is a bit more challenging when you eat out, but you can do it. (You have to! Who wants to cook every night?) You probably realize that, at many restaurants, one "serving" of anything—from appetizer to dessert—is more like two (or three, or four!). So, ask your server to bring you a to-go box along with your meal and wrap up half of your food to take home before you even dig in to the rest. In addition, the visual guide on page 23 can help you visualize proper portion sizes when your measuring tools aren't handy. Just make a photocopy and tuck it in your purse or wallet, then refer to it as you need to until you've perfected your eyeballing technique.

Once you've reached your goal weight, you might switch to measuring just grains (such as pasta, rice, and breakfast cereal) and fats (such as nuts, oils, and salad dressings). Think about it: Few people gain weight by eating lots of low-calorie, nutrient-dense fruits and vegetables. Grains and fats, on the other hand, can blow your calorie budget pretty quickly. Get lax about their portions and you could add hundreds of calories to your daily intake. An extra ⅓ cup of berries or broccoli is far less risky—and besides, their high fiber content makes eating too much of them far less likely.

DTOUR How-To #3: Feast on the Fat-Fighting 4

On DTOUR, the majority of foods that you'll weigh and measure are *whole foods*. In other words, they're in or close to their natural state, with nothing added—no sugars, fats, or artificial anything. Oatmeal and strawberries are whole foods; cream-filled oatmeal pies and strawberry toaster pastries are not.

Whole foods also happen to be the best sources of our Fat-Fighting 4. Stick with the DTOUR menus and you're sure to get at least—if not more than—the recommended daily intake of each of these supernutrients. Here's a snapshot of how they'll help you achieve your weight-loss and blood sugar goals; for more detailed descriptions, turn back to page 6.

Fiber. All whole foods are high in fiber, which satisfies your hunger, helps reduce the number of calories absorbed by your body, and keeps your blood sugar from skyrocketing after a meal. Along with fruits, veggies, and whole grains, don't overlook another outstanding fiber source: beans. Red or black, pink or speckled, dry or canned, beans are nutritional gems. One cup of cooked beans provides a whopping 13 grams of fiber and 15 grams of protein, with zero saturated fat. They also offer respectable doses of calcium and another diabetes fighter, magnesium.

Calcium and vitamin D. On DTOUR, you'll easily take in about 1,300 milligrams of calcium and about 400 IU of vitamin D every day from a variety of sources—not just dairy. If you choose soy milk, make sure it's fortified with at least 30 percent of the Daily Value of calcium per serving.

Since the Daily Value of calcium is 1,000 milligrams, a serving of soy milk should supply roughly 300 milligrams.

Omega-3 fatty acids. Put fish on your dish—along with walnuts, flaxseed, and tofu. Research from Spain suggests that it's easier to stay slim when you're consuming omega-3s and monounsaturated fats. In contrast, the omega-6 fats (prevalent in corn oil and baked goods) cause the ab fat to pile on.

Incidentally, when you follow DTOUR, you'll automatically limit your intake of trans fats. These bad-for-you fats, which are found mostly in processed foods and bakery products, have no redeeming nutritional value.

DTOUR How-To #4: Eat Every 3 Hours

If you're accustomed to the standard three square meals a day, DTOUR will ask you to up the ante. Our menus provide for three meals and two snacks every day, each containing a mix of complex carbs, lean protein, and beneficial fats, plus a healthy dose of each of the Fat-Fighting 4.

When you eat smaller meals more often, your blood sugar stays on an even keel, which in turn helps tame hunger and control weight. Studies have shown that even among people with essentially the same caloric intakes, those who eat fewer times per day are likely to weigh more.

Small, frequent meals also keep your metabolism humming. You can think of your metabolism as a wood-burning fire: If you don't stoke the flames and add wood at regular intervals, it eventually goes out. The same is true for your body. Stoke it with nutritious fuel every few hours and you'll keep your metabolism elevated, your blood sugar stable, and your body operating at its peak.

There is one corollary to DTOUR's five-meals-and-snacks-a-day rule, and it's this: *You must eat breakfast.* It really is the most important meal of the day, especially if you want to lose weight. When you skip your morning meal, you may crave more high-calorie foods later in the day. As a result, you may eat more throughout the day than you would otherwise.

A final note: While it's important for everyone to eat approximately every 3 hours throughout the day, it's especially so if you're on diabetes medication. Waiting more than 5 hours between meals, or skipping a meal entirely, can cause your blood sugar to plunge.

PERFECT PORTIONS: YOUR CHEAT SHEET

Knowing what to eat is half the battle. But to lose weight and manage your blood sugar, you need to know how much to eat, too. The list below provides the correct serving sizes for the top food sources of the Fat-Fighting 4.

CALCIUM AND VITAMIN D

Cheese, light or nonfat, 1 ounce	Low-fat cottage cheese, ½ cup	calcium and Vitamin D, 8 ounces	Yogurt, flavored light fat-free or low-fat, 6 ounces (⅔ cup)
Fat-free milk, 8 ounces	Low-fat milk (skim or 1%), 8 ounces	Yogurt, fat-free plain, 8 ounces (1 cup)	
Fat-free ricotta cheese, ⅓ cup	Low-fat soy or rice milk fortified with		

FIBER

Beans and legumes (Serving size = ½ cup cooked)

Black beans	Garbanzo beans (chickpeas)	Lentils	Navy beans
Dried peas	Kidney beans	Lima beans	Pinto beans

Fruits

Apple, pear (1 whole small or medium fruit)	Banana (½)	Canned, cooked, chopped fruit (½ cup)	Citrus fruits (1 whole small or medium fruit)
	Berries (½ cup)		

Soy products (Serving size = ½ cup cooked)

Miso	Soybeans	Tempeh	Tofu

Starchy vegetables (Serving size = ½ cup unless otherwise noted)

Corn	Peas	Sweet potato or yam, baked, plain, 1 small or ½ large	Sweet potato or yam, plain, mashed
Lima beans	Potato, baked, 1 small or ½ large		

Vegetables (Serving size = 1 cup raw, ½ cup cooked)

Artichoke	Carrots	Green peppers	Spinach
Asparagus	Cauliflower	Lettuce	Squash
Broccoli	Celery	Mushrooms	Tomato
Brussels sprouts	Cucumber	Onions	Zucchini
Cabbage	Green beans	Pumpkin	

Whole grains (Serving size = ½ cup cooked)

Barley	Oatmeal	Rice, brown or wild (⅓ cup)	Spelt
Buckwheat	Quinoa	Rye	Whole wheat
Millet			Whole wheat pasta

Whole grain products

Bread, 1 slice	Cereal, cooked, ½ cup	English muffin, ½	Rice cakes, 2
Bread, reduced-calorie, 2 slices	Cereal, ready to eat, 1 ounce	Pita or wrap, ½ of 8-inch diameter	Tortilla, 6-inch diameter

OMEGA-3 FATTY ACIDS

Fish Serving size = 3 ounces cooked

Catfish	Haddock	Shellfish (shrimp, crab, lobster)	Tuna
	Salmon		

Plants

Canola oil, 1 tablespoon	Nuts: almonds, peanuts, walnut halves, 1 ounce	Olive oil, 1 tablespoon	Seeds: pumpkin, sesame, sunflower, ½ ounce
Flaxseed, 1 tablespoon		Safflower oil, 1 tablespoon	

HANDY PORTION CONTROL

Feel sheepish about carrying your measuring cups and spoons into your favorite restaurant? Well, we do, too. So here's the next best thing: a (literally) handy guide to estimating portion sizes.

HAND	EQUIVALENT	FOODS	CALORIES
Fist	1 c	Rice	200
		Pasta	75
		Fruit	40
Palm	3 oz	Meat	160
		Fish	160
		Poultry	160
Handful	1 oz	Nuts	170
		Raisins	85
2 handfuls	1 oz	Chips	150
		Popcorn	120
		Pretzels	100
Thumb	1 oz	Peanut butter	170
		Hard cheese	100
Thumb tip	1 tsp	Cooking oil	40
		Mayonnaise	35
		Butter	35
		Sugar	15

THE 2-WEEK FAST START

For the next 2 weeks, we've made eating healthfully as effortless as possible. Every day of the Fast Start features a complete menu of our Awesome 4some meals and snacks. Preparation is a breeze; every recipe equals one serving, so you just need to measure or count the ingredients.

For ease of use, we've broken out the 1,400- and 1,600-calorie plans into separate menus for each day. Really, though, they aren't all that different. On either plan, you'll be getting approximately 40 percent of your calories from carbohydrates, 25 percent from protein, and 35 percent from fat. Saturated fat—the bad-for-you kind—accounts for no more than 7 percent of your total caloric intake.

Whichever calorie level you choose, you're sure to get your daily fix of the Fat-Fighting 4. On the 1,400-calorie plan, our Awesome 4some meals and snacks deliver about 26 grams of fiber, 1,100 milligrams of calcium, 144 IU of vitamin D, and 2.5 grams of omega-3s per day. These numbers are just a tad higher on the 1,600-calorie plan, which averages 29 grams of fiber, 1,200 milligrams of calcium, 165 IU of vitamin D, and 2.7 grams of omega-3s per day.

To get the best results from the Fast Start, you'll want to follow these few simple rules.

Pick the right plan. Women who are short in stature or who have been fairly sedentary should go with the 1,400-calorie plan. The 1,600-calorie plan is best for women who are tall or very active and for men of all builds and fitness levels. Another option is to try the 1,600-calorie plan for 1 week. If you lose weight, stick with it; if not, switch plans.

Follow the menus exactly. We've designed all of the DTOUR menus to ensure that you're eating about every 3 hours—which will keep your tummy happy and your blood sugar steady—and that you're getting the maximum benefit from the Fat-Fighting 4. Portion sizes are critical. Use your measuring tools throughout the Fast Start; before you know it, you'll be able to eyeball proper portions.

Choose the best ingredients for your Awesome 4some meals and snacks.

◆ Each day, you'll fill up on fiber-rich whole foods. Fresh fruits and veggies are preferable, but frozen fruits (without added sugar) and veggies (without butter or sauces) contain as much fiber and nutrients as fresh. For salads, we recommend dark, leafy greens (romaine, spinach leaves), which contain more nutrients than iceberg lettuce, but use whatever type you prefer.

◆ For these 2 weeks, use a scale to weigh fruit to get an idea of what a serving looks like.

◆ Select no-sugar-added, fat-free or low-fat yogurts that contain no more than 100 calories and no more than 15 grams of total carbohydrates per serving. Look for brands enriched with vitamin D (not all are).

◆ Opt for fat-free milk or low-fat soy or rice beverage fortified with calcium and vitamin D.

◆ Opt for soft tub or liquid margarines with zero grams of trans fats and no more than 1 gram of saturated fat per serving.

◆ If you use canned beans, rinse them thoroughly to remove as much sodium as possible.

◆ It's fine to enjoy your cup of coffee or tea at breakfast. Black is best, but you can add a sprinkle of sugar-free sweetener and a splash of fat-free milk or low-fat soy or rice beverage if you like.

◆ You may have sparkling water or reduced-calorie beverages (diet lemonade, for example), as long as they contain no more than 20 calories per serving.

◆ For light ice cream, look for products that provide no more than 2 grams of saturated fat and no more than 20 grams of total carbohydrate per serving.

Now, let's get started!

1,400 CALORIES

BREAKFAST

❒ Veggie omelet: Heat 1 teaspoon canola, peanut, or olive oil in a skillet. Add ¼ cup egg substitute (or 1 egg white); ½ cup spinach leaves; ½ cup chopped mushrooms; and as much onion, garlic, and herbs as desired. Cook over low heat until set. Top with ¼ cup reduced-fat cheese.

❒ ½ cup fat-free milk or low-fat, calcium-enriched soy or rice beverage

❒ 1 slice reduced-calorie whole grain toast spread with 1 teaspoon trans-free canola margarine

LUNCH

❒ Tuna sandwich: Mix 2 ounces water-packed tuna with 2 tablespoons reduced-fat mayonnaise (or 2 teaspoons regular mayonnaise). Spread on 1 slice whole grain bread *or* 2 slices reduced-calorie whole grain bread. Top with green or red leaf lettuce; 1 small tomato (½ cup), sliced; and 4 large black olives, chopped.

SNACK

❒ 8 ounces (1 cup) fat-free plain yogurt *or* 6 ounces (⅔ cup) no-sugar-added, fat-free or low-fat flavored yogurt, topped with ¾ cup fresh blueberries or blackberries

DINNER

❒ 3 ounces grilled chicken breast with garlic herb seasoning (such as Mrs. Dash)

❒ ⅔ cup cooked brown or wild rice

❒ 2 cups grilled or roasted vegetables (mushrooms, onions, zucchini, yellow squash, bell peppers) tossed with 2 teaspoons olive oil and salt-free herb seasoning to taste

SNACK

❒ 1 small apple (4 ounces), sliced, spread with 2 teaspoons peanut butter

1,600 CALORIES

BREAKFAST

❒ Veggie omelet: Heat 2 teaspoons canola, peanut, or olive oil in a skillet. Add ½ cup egg substitute (or 2 egg whites), ½ cup spinach leaves, ½ cup chopped mushrooms, 2 tablespoons chopped onion, 1 teaspoon chopped or minced garlic, and herbs as desired. Cook over low heat until set. Top with 2 tablespoons shredded reduced-fat cheese.

❒ 1 slice whole grain toast or 2 slices reduced-calorie whole grain toast spread with 1 teaspoon trans-free canola margarine

❒ 1 cup fat-free milk or low-fat, calcium-enriched soy or rice beverage

LUNCH

❒ Tuna sandwich: Mix 3 ounces water-packed tuna with 2 tablespoons reduced-fat mayonnaise (or 1 tablespoon regular mayonnaise). Spread on 1 slice whole grain bread *or* 2 slices reduced-calorie whole grain bread. Top with green or red leaf lettuce; 1 small tomato (½ cup), sliced; and 4 large black olives, chopped.

SNACK

❒ 8 ounces (1 cup) fat-free plain *or* 6 ounces (⅔ cup) no-sugar-added, fat-free or low-fat flavored yogurt, topped with ¾ cup fresh blueberries or blackberries and 1 tablespoon chopped walnuts

DINNER

❒ 3 ounces grilled chicken breast with garlic herb seasoning (such as Mrs. Dash)

❒ ⅔ cup cooked brown or wild rice

❒ 2 cups grilled or roasted vegetables (mushrooms, onions, zucchini, yellow squash, bell peppers) prepared in 1 tablespoon olive oil, sprinkled with Mrs. Dash or other salt-free herb seasoning

SNACK

❒ 1 small apple (4 ounces), sliced, spread with 2 teaspoons peanut butter

HOW DID YOU DO?

BALANCE YOUR BLOOD SUGAR

	TIME	READING
CHECK 1		
CHECK 2		
CHECK 3		
CHECK 4		
CHECK 5		

MEASURE YOURSELF

Starting weight: _____ pounds

Starting waistline: _____ inches

> Success is the sum of small efforts, repeated day in and day out.
> —ROBERT J. COLLIER

SUCCEED ALL DAY

To think before you binge, use the HALT technique. Before you scarf down that box of mini-doughnuts or plow through a bag of chips, ask yourself, "Do I want to eat this because I'm *hungry, angry, lonely,* or *tired*?" Often, simply knowing what's driving your urge to overeat can short-circuit it.

Take a "gratitude break." Tick off one thing or person you're grateful to have in your life. Are you grateful that the sun is shining after days of rain? Duck out of the office to soak up the sunshine. Do you appreciate your supportive spouse? Send an e-mail to say so—and don't forget to say why.

1,400 CALORIES

BREAKFAST

❐ 1 cup cooked oatmeal topped with 2 tablespoons walnut halves (about 8) and ½ teaspoon ground cinnamon and/or 1 teaspoon sugar substitute

❐ ½ cup fat-free milk or low-fat, calcium-enriched soy or rice beverage

LUNCH

❐ Chicken salad: Mix 2 cups mixed greens, ½ cup chopped tomato, ½ cup sliced cucumber, and ¼ cup chopped carrot. Top with 2 ounces chicken breast. Drizzle with avocado yogurt dressing (¼ cup mashed avocado, ½ cup fat-free plain yogurt, and vinegar and/or herbs to taste).

❐ 1 ounce (2 slices) whole grain crispbread crackers

SNACK

❐ 1 ounce string cheese

❐ 1 small pear or other fruit (4 ounces)

DINNER

❐ 1 cup Progresso Healthy Classics or Campbell's Healthy Request canned beef barley soup

❐ Spinach salad: Toss 3 cups fresh spinach with 1 tablespoon each olive oil and balsamic vinegar dressing. Top with 2 tablespoons shredded reduced-fat mozzarella cheese.

❐ 1 slice whole grain bread or 2 slices reduced-calorie, high-fiber whole grain bread

SNACK

❐ 1 medium orange

❐ 3 tablespoons unsalted raw cashews (about 18)

1,600 CALORIES

BREAKFAST

❐ 1 cup cooked oatmeal topped with 3 tablespoons walnut halves (about 12) and cinnamon and/or sugar substitute to taste

❐ 1 cup fat-free milk or low-fat, calcium-enriched soy or rice beverage

LUNCH

❐ Chicken salad: Mix 2 cups mixed greens, ½ cup chopped tomato, ½ cup sliced cucumber, and ¼ cup chopped carrot. Top with 3 ounces chicken breast. Drizzle with avocado yogurt dressing (¼ cup mashed avocado, ½ cup fat-free plain yogurt, and vinegar and/or herbs to taste).

❐ 1 ounce (2 slices) whole grain crispbread crackers

❐ 2 tablespoons hummus

SNACK

❐ 1 ounce mozzarella string cheese

❐ 1 small pear or other fruit (4 ounces)

DINNER

❐ 1½ cup Progresso Healthy Classics or Campbell's Healthy Request canned beef barley soup

❐ Spinach salad: Toss 2 cups fresh spinach with 1 tablespoon each olive oil and balsamic vinegar dressing. Top with 2 tablespoons shredded reduced-fat mozzarella cheese.

❐ 1 slice whole grain bread or 2 slices reduced-calorie, high-fiber whole grain bread

SNACK

❐ 1 medium orange

❐ 2 tablespoons unsalted raw cashews (about 12)

HOW DID YOU DO?

BALANCE YOUR BLOOD SUGAR

	TIME	READING
CHECK 1		
CHECK 2		
CHECK 3		
CHECK 4		
CHECK 5		

The only way to discover the limits of the possible is to go beyond them into the impossible.
—ARTHUR C. CLARKE

SUCCEED ALL DAY
Go cold turkey on trigger foods. Can't have just one cheese curl or chocolate-chip cookie? Indulging a craving affects your brain the same way that thinking about cocaine affects an addict's brain. That surprising comparison comes from studies conducted by researchers at Brookhaven National Laboratory in Upton, New York, who scanned the brains of 12 people as they sampled their favorite foods.

Develop a bedtime routine. Do the same thing every night before going to sleep. For example, take a warm bath and then read for 10 minutes before going to bed. Soon you'll connect these activities with sleeping, and doing them will help make you sleepy.

1,400 CALORIES

BREAKFAST

❏ Peanut butter banana toast: Spread 1 slice reduced-calorie whole grain toast with 2 tablespoons all-natural peanut butter and ½ medium banana, sliced.

❏ ½ cup fat-free milk or low-fat, calcium-enriched soy or rice beverage

LUNCH

❏ Mixed-Up Salad: Mix 2 cups vegetable greens, ¾ cup 1% cottage cheese, and ½ cup mandarin orange slices with 2 tablespoons light Italian salad dressing. Top with 2 tablespoons chopped unsalted raw almonds (about 12) or walnut halves (about 8).

❏ 5 whole grain crackers (such as Triscuits)

SNACK

❏ 6 ounces no-sugar-added, fat-free or low-fat yogurt

❏ 2 tablespoons chopped walnuts

DINNER

❏ Grilled fish tacos: Tuck 1 ounce grilled salmon or other fish and ½ cup shredded cabbage seasoned with rice vinegar into each of 2 corn tortillas. Top each with 1 tablespoon reduced-fat sour cream.

❏ Grilled or roasted vegetables: Marinate 2 cups eggplant, mushrooms, green beans, and onion in 2 tablespoons light Italian dressing. Grill or roast.

SNACK

❏ 2 tablespoons hummus

❏ 2 rye crisp crackers

1,600 CALORIES

BREAKFAST

❏ Peanut butter banana toast: Spread 1 slice reduced-calorie whole grain toast with 2 tablespoons all-natural peanut butter and ½ medium banana, sliced.

❏ 1 cup fat-free milk or low-fat, calcium-enriched soy or rice beverage

LUNCH

❏ Mixed-Up Salad: Mix 2 cups vegetable greens, 1 cup 1% cottage cheese, and ½ cup mandarin orange slices with 2 tablespoons light Italian dressing. Top with 2 tablespoons chopped unsalted raw almonds (about 12) or walnut halves (about 8).

❏ 5 whole-grain crackers (such as Triscuits)

SNACK

❏ 6 ounces no-sugar-added, fat-free or low-fat flavored yogurt

❏ 2 tablespoons raw walnut halves

DINNER

❏ Grilled fish tacos: Tuck 1½ ounces grilled salmon or other fish and ½ cup shredded cabbage seasoned with rice vinegar into each of 2 corn tortillas. Top each with 1 tablespoon reduced-fat sour cream.

❏ Grilled or roasted vegetables: Marinate 2 cups eggplant, mushrooms, green beans, and onion in 2 tablespoons light Italian dressing and 1 teaspoon olive oil. Grill or roast.

SNACK

❏ 2 tablespoons hummus

❏ 2 rye crisp crackers

HOW DID YOU DO?

BALANCE YOUR BLOOD SUGAR

	TIME	READING
CHECK 1		
CHECK 2		
CHECK 3		
CHECK 4		
CHECK 5		

You cannot plough
a field by turning it
over in your mind.
—AUTHOR UNKNOWN

SUCCEED ALL DAY

Let loose with laughter—or tears. Both are stress melters. When you laugh, your muscles go limp and the knots unkink. Tears help cleanse the body of substances that accumulate in times of stress.

Turn in only when you're sleepy. If you can't fall asleep within 15 to 20 minutes, get up and leave your bedroom. Go into the living room and read until you're tired again. Or sit in a chair and think pleasant thoughts: a dream vacation or standing by a waterfall. This should help calm you so you can return to bed and sleep.

1,400 CALORIES

BREAKFAST

❏ 1 ounce (about 1 cup) flaxseed-enriched whole grain cereal

❏ 1 cup fat-free milk or low-fat, calcium-enriched soy or rice beverage

❏ 2 tablespoons unsalted raw almonds (about 17)

LUNCH

❏ Cheese quesadilla: Place 2 ounces reduced-fat cheese on 1 whole wheat tortilla. Fold tortilla in half and cook in small skillet over medium heat until cheese melts and tortilla is browned on both sides. (You can also microwave on medium power for 30 to 45 seconds.) Garnish with 1½ cups chopped lettuce and tomato, ¼ cup salsa, 2 tablespoons avocado, and 1 tablespoon reduced-fat sour cream.

SNACK

❏ 1 medium banana spread with 1 tablespoon all-natural peanut butter

DINNER

❏ 3 ounces oven-roasted beef or pork tenderloin

❏ 2 cups roasted vegetables (½ cup potato plus 1½ cups nonstarchy vegetables, such as green beans, bell peppers, eggplant, zucchini or yellow squash, onion, and garlic) tossed in 1 tablespoon olive oil and baked at 400°F for 30 to 40 minutes.

SNACK

❏ 2 whole grain fig cookies

❏ 1 cup fat-free milk or low-fat, calcium-enriched soy or rice beverage

1,600 CALORIES

BREAKFAST

❏ 1 ounce (about 1 cup) flaxseed-enriched whole grain cereal

❏ 1 cup fat-free milk or low-fat, calcium-enriched soy or rice beverage

❏ 3 tablespoons chopped almonds

LUNCH

❏ Cheese quesadilla: Place 1 ounce shredded chicken and 2 ounces reduced-fat cheese on two 6-inch or one 12-inch whole wheat tortilla. Fold tortilla in half and cook in small skillet over medium heat until cheese melts and tortilla is browned on both sides. (You can also microwave on medium power for 30 to 45 seconds.) Garnish with 2 cups chopped lettuce and tomato, ¼ cup salsa, 2 tablespoons avocado, and 1 tablespoon reduced-fat sour cream.

SNACK

❏ 1 medium banana spread with 1 tablespoon all-natural peanut butter

DINNER

❏ 3 ounces oven-roasted beef or pork tenderloin

❏ 2 cups roasted vegetables (½ cup potato plus 1½ cups nonstarchy vegetables, such as green beans, bell peppers, eggplant, zucchini or yellow squash, onion, and garlic) tossed in 1 tablespoon olive oil and baked at 400°F for 30 to 40 minutes.

SNACK

❏ 2 whole grain fig cookies

❏ 1 cup fat-free milk or low-fat, calcium-enriched soy or rice beverage

HOW DID YOU DO?

BALANCE YOUR BLOOD SUGAR

	TIME	READING
CHECK 1		
CHECK 2		
CHECK 3		
CHECK 4		
CHECK 5		

Our greatest glory
is not in never falling,
but in rising every
time we fall.
—CONFUCIUS

SUCCEED ALL DAY

Choose the right craving "cure." To defang a craving, identify your current emotion (e.g., bored, anxious, angry) and complete this sentence: "I feel _____ because of _____." Now, find an activity that releases that emotion. If you're stressed, for example, channel your nervous energy into cleaning out a closet or tackling yard work.

Try moving meditation. Qigong (chee-gung), an active Chinese meditation routine incorporating fluid, dance-like movements and controlled breathing, elicits the body's relaxation response, studies have found. Classes often are held at YMCAs, gyms, and community centers. Find a local instructor at the National Qigong Association's Web site, www.nqa.org.

1,400 CALORIES

BREAKFAST

☐ ½ whole grain bagel spread with 1 tablespoon low-fat cream cheese and 1 teaspoon 100 percent fruit spread

☐ 1 cup fat-free milk or low-fat, calcium-enriched soy or rice beverage

LUNCH

☐ Taco No Taco Salad: Mix 2 ounces grilled fish, chicken, or lean beef with ⅓ cup brown rice and ½ cup cooked red, black, or pinto beans. Top with 1 tablespoon shredded reduced-fat cheese. Microwave on medium power for 45 seconds. Top with ½ cup salsa and 1 tablespoon reduced-fat sour cream. Serve over 2 cups mixed lettuce greens.

SNACK

☐ ¼ cup walnuts or pecans mixed with 6 ounces low-fat plain yogurt or light yogurt sweetened with noncalorie sweetner. Sprinkle with ground cinnamon to taste.

DINNER

☐ 3 ounces grilled salmon

☐ ½ cup fruit salsa (chopped melon and mango)

☐ 2 cups spinach leaves with 2 tablespoons chopped unsalted raw pecans and ¾ sliced red onion

☐ 1 tablespoon oil-and-vinegar dressing

☐ 1 cup fat-free milk or low-fat, calcium-enriched soy or rice beverage

SNACK

☐ 1 ounce spreadable reduced-fat cheese

☐ 1 medium pear, sliced

1,600 CALORIES

BREAKFAST

☐ ½ whole grain bagel spread with 2 tablespoons natural peanut butter

☐ 1 cup fat-free milk or low-fat, calcium-enriched soy or rice beverage

LUNCH

☐ Taco No Taco Salad: Mix 3 ounces grilled fish, chicken, or lean beef with ⅓ cup brown rice and ½ cup cooked red, black, or pinto beans. Top with 2 tablespoons shredded reduced-fat cheese. Microwave on medium power for 45 seconds. Top with ½ cup salsa and 2 tablespoons reduced-fat sour cream. Serve over 2 cups mixed lettuce greens.

SNACK

☐ ¼ cup walnuts or pecans mixed with 6 ounces low-fat plain yogurt or light yogurt sweetened with noncalorie sweetner. Sprinkle with ground cinnamon to taste.

DINNER

☐ 3 ounces grilled salmon

☐ ½ cup fruit salsa (chopped melon and mango)

☐ 2 cups spinach leaves with 2 tablespoons chopped unsalted raw pecans and ¼ cup sliced red onions

☐ 1 tablespoon oil-and-vinegar dressing or 2 tablespoons light Italian dressing

☐ 1 slice reduced-calorie, high-fiber bread

☐ 1 cup fat-free milk or low-fat, calcium-enriched soy or rice beverage

SNACK

☐ 1 ounce spreadable reduced-fat cheese

☐ 1 medium pear, sliced

HOW DID YOU DO?

BALANCE YOUR BLOOD SUGAR

	TIME	READING
CHECK 1		
CHECK 2		
CHECK 3		
CHECK 4		
CHECK 5		

Nothing great was
ever achieved without
enthusiasm.
—RALPH WALDO EMERSON

SUCCEED ALL DAY

Practice safe cravings. Plan ways to enjoy craved foods in controlled portions. Order a slice of pizza instead of a whole pie, or share a piece of restaurant cheesecake with two friends.

Stub out the butts. Nicotine stimulates the nervous system and disturbs sleep. But if you're a habitual smoker who can't fall or stay asleep, insomnia is the least of your worries. Quit. Today. You'll help protect your health and sleep better, too. At the very least, avoid nicotine within 1 hour of bedtime.

1,400 CALORIES

BREAKFAST

❒ Super White Egg: Heat 1 teaspoon canola oil in a small skillet. Add 1 whole egg and then 1 egg white or ¼ cup egg substitute around the outside of the whole egg. Cook over low heat until set. Top with 2 tablespoons chopped tomato or salsa.

❒ 1 slice reduced-calorie, high-fiber whole grain toast spread with 1 teaspoon trans-free canola margarine

❒ 1 cup fat-free milk or low-fat, calcium-enriched soy or rice beverage

SNACK

❒ 6 ounces no-sugar-added, fat-free or low-fat flavored yogurt

❒ 4 dried apricot halves

LUNCH

❒ Pile 'Er High Turkey and Ham Sandwich: Pile 1 ounce *each* sliced ham, turkey, and low-fat cheese on 1 slice reduced-calorie, high-fiber whole wheat bread. Spread 1 additional slice bread with 1 tablespoon reduced-fat mayonnaise (or 1 teaspoon regular mayonnaise) and 1 tablespoon mustard, if desired. Top with ½ cup shredded romaine lettuce and ½ tomato, sliced.

❒ 8 baby carrots dipped in 1 tablespoon low-fat ranch dressing

DINNER

❒ Beef- or Chicken-Broccoli Stir-Fry: Stir-fry 4 ounces lean beef or chicken breast and 1 cup broccoli, 1 cup carrots, and ½ cup onion in 1 tablespoon olive oil and 2 tablespoons low-sodium teriyaki sauce. Serve over ⅓ cup cooked brown or wild rice.

SNACK

❒ 3 cups light microwave popcorn

❒ 16 ounces sugar-free seltzer water

1,600 CALORIES

BREAKFAST

❒ Super White Egg: Heat 1 tablespoon canola oil in a small skillet. Add 1 whole egg and then 1 egg white or ¼ cup egg substitute around the outside of the whole egg. Cook over low heat until set. Top with 2 tablespoons chopped tomato or salsa.

❒ 2 slices reduced-calorie, high-fiber whole grain toast spread with 1 teaspoon trans-free canola margarine

❒ 1 cup fat-free milk or low-fat, calcium-enriched soy or rice beverage

SNACK

❒ 6 ounces no-sugar-added, fat-free or low-fat flavored yogurt

❒ 4 dried apricot halves

LUNCH

❒ Pile 'Er High Turkey and Ham Sandwich: Pile 1 ounce sliced ham, 2 ounces sliced turkey, and 1 ounce sliced reduced-fat cheese on 1 slice reduced-calorie, high-fiber whole wheat bread. Spread 1 additional slice bread with 1 tablespoon reduced-fat mayonnaise (or 1 teaspoon regular mayonnaise) and 1 tablespoon mustard, if desired. Top with ½ cup shredded romaine lettuce and ½ tomato, sliced.

❒ 16 baby carrots dipped in 1 tablespoon low-fat ranch dressing

DINNER

❒ Beef- or Chicken-Broccoli Stir-Fry: Stir-fry 4 ounces lean beef or chicken breast and 2 cups broccoli, carrots, and onion in 1 tablespoon olive oil and 2 tablespoons low-sodium teriyaki sauce. Serve over ⅔ cup cooked brown or wild rice

SNACK

❒ 3 cups light microwave popcorn

❒ 16 ounces lemon-lime seltzer water

HOW DID YOU DO?

BALANCE YOUR BLOOD SUGAR

	TIME	READING
CHECK 1		
CHECK 2		
CHECK 3		
CHECK 4		
CHECK 5		

First say to yourself
what you would be;
and then do what you
have to do.

—EPICTETUS

SUCCEED ALL DAY

Reach out a helping hand. Under stress, we tend to focus on ourselves. But helping someone else in distress—even if it's just running an elderly neighbor to the store—can help us put our own worries in perspective. **Move the TV out of your bedroom.** Your spouse may grumble, but if you're a chronic late-night talk-show buff, go cold turkey. The bed and bedroom are for sleep and sex. That's it. No reading. No talking on the telephone. No worrying.

1,400 CALORIES

BREAKFAST

☐ 3 buckwheat or whole wheat pancakes (6" diameter) spread with 1 teaspoon trans-free canola margarine and 1 tablespoon 100 percent fruit spread *or* 2 tablespoons sugar-free syrup, if desired, and sprinkled with 1 tablespoon chopped walnuts

☐ 8 ounces fat-free milk or low-fat, calcium-enriched soy or rice beverage

LUNCH

☐ Chicken Caesar salad: Top 3 cups romaine lettuce with 2 ounces skinless cooked chicken and ½ cup mandarin oranges packed in juice or water, drained. Drizzle on 2 tablespoons light Caesar dressing and top with 1 tablespoon Parmesan cheese.

☐ 1 ounce whole grain crackers

SNACK

☐ 1 cup apple slices

☐ 2 tablespoons walnut halves

DINNER

☐ 4 ounces (3 ounces cooked) top sirloin, grilled or broiled

☐ ½ oven-baked potato (about 3 ounces): Preheat oven to 400°F. Slice potato lengthwise, drizzle cut side with 1 teaspoon olive oil, and bake with cut side down for 30 minutes or until brown.

☐ Garlic roasted asparagus: Toss 10 medium (5-7") asparagus spears or 1 cup cut asparagus in 1 teaspoon olive oil and chopped garlic to taste. Roast with the potato for 20 minutes.

SNACK

☐ 1 cup fat-free milk or low-fat, calcium-enriched soy or rice beverage

☐ 5 vanilla wafers or 3 graham cracker squares (1½ sheets)

1,600 CALORIES

BREAKFAST

☐ 4 buckwheat or whole wheat pancakes (6" diameter) spread with 1 teaspoon trans-free canola margarine and 1 tablespoon 100 percent fruit spread *or* 2 tablespoons sugar-free syrup, if desired, and sprinkled with 1 tablespoon chopped walnuts

☐ 8 ounces fat-free milk or low-fat, calcium-enriched soy or rice beverage

LUNCH

☐ Chicken Caesar salad: Top 3 cups romaine lettuce with 3 ounces skinless cooked chicken and ½ cup mandarin oranges packed in juice or water, drained. Drizzle on 2 tablespoons light Caesar dressing and top with 1 tablespoon Parmesan cheese.

☐ 1 ounce whole grain crackers

SNACK

☐ 1 cup apple slices

☐ ¼ cup walnut halves (about 16)

DINNER

☐ 4 ounces (3 ounces cooked) top sirloin, grilled or broiled

☐ 1 small oven-baked potato: Preheat oven to 400°F. Slice potato lengthwise, drizzle cut side with 1 teaspoon olive oil, and bake with cut side down for 30 minutes or until brown.

☐ Garlic roasted asparagus: Toss 10 medium (5-7") asparagus spears or 1 cup cut asparagus in 1 teaspoon olive oil and chopped garlic to taste. Roast with the potato for 20 minutes.

SNACK

☐ 1 cup fat-free milk or low-fat, calcium-enriched soy or rice beverage

☐ 5 vanilla wafers or 3 graham cracker squares

HOW DID YOU DO?

BALANCE YOUR BLOOD SUGAR

	TIME	READING
CHECK 1		
CHECK 2		
CHECK 3		
CHECK 4		
CHECK 5		

SUCCEED ALL DAY

Eliminate sensory cues. Smells, sights, and sounds are all powerful triggers. So whether you're, say, paying bills or reading the newspaper, be sure to station yourself far away from the kitchen and the cupboard full of snacks.

Recite the Serenity Prayer. This prayer is a time-tested way to get calm quick: "God, grant me the serenity to accept the things I cannot change, the courage to change the things I can, and the wisdom to know the difference."

If you let your fear of consequence prevent you from following your deepest instinct, your life will be safe, expedient and thin.
—KATHARINE BUTLER HATHAWAY

1,400 CALORIES

BREAKFAST

☐ Fruit smoothie: In a blender, combine 1 cup fat-free milk or low-fat, calcium-enriched soy or rice beverage; 6 ounces (³⁄₄ cup) fat-free plain yogurt; ½ cup sliced or chopped strawberries; 2 tablespoons chopped walnuts; and 4 tablespoons flaxseed meal. Add ground cinnamon and/or sugar substitute to taste. Blend 15 seconds.

LUNCH

☐ Tuna melt: Preheat oven to 450°F. Toast ½ whole grain English muffin. Combine ¼ cup (1 ounce) water-packed tuna, drained; 1 tablespoon reduced-fat mayonnaise (or 1 teaspoon regular mayonnaise); 1 tablespoon minced dill pickle and/or chopped celery; and 1 ounce reduced-fat cheese. Spoon mixture onto toasted muffin. Place in oven for 5 to 10 minutes or microwave on high power for 30 seconds, or until cheese melts.

☐ 8 baby carrots dipped in 1 tablespoon reduced-fat ranch dressing

☐ 1 cup fat-free milk or low-fat, calcium-enriched soy or rice beverage

SNACK

☐ 1 medium orange or tangerine

☐ 2 tablespoons unsalted dry-roasted almonds (about 12)

DINNER

☐ 3 ounces chicken breast, grilled or roasted, with 2 tablespoons barbecue sauce

☐ 1 slice sourdough bread spread with 1 teaspoon olive oil and minced garlic to taste and toasted

☐ Colorful Coleslaw: Mix 1 cup shredded red and green cabbage and carrots with 2 tablespoons reduced-fat (or 1 tablespoon regular) coleslaw dressing.

SNACK

☐ 2 squares graham crackers (1 sheet)

☐ 1 tablespoon all-natural peanut butter

1,600 CALORIES

BREAKFAST

☐ Fruit smoothie: In a blender, combine 1 cup fat-free milk or low-fat, calcium-enriched soy or rice beverage; 6 ounces (³⁄₄ cup) fat-free plain yogurt; ½ cup sliced or chopped strawberries; 2 tablespoons chopped walnuts; and 2 tablespoons flaxseed meal. Add ground cinnamon and/or sugar substitute to taste. Blend 15 seconds.

LUNCH

☐ Tuna melt: Preheat oven to 450°F. Toast 1 whole grain English muffin. Combine ½ cup (2 ounces) water-packed tuna, drained; 2 tablespoons reduced-fat mayonnaise (or 1 tablespoon regular mayonnaise); 1 tablespoon minced dill pickle and/or chopped celery; and 1 ounce reduced-fat cheese. Spoon mixture onto both halves of toasted muffin. Place in oven for 5 to 10 minutes or microwave on high power for 30 seconds, or until cheese melts.

☐ 16 baby carrots dipped in 1 tablespoon reduced-fat ranch dressing

☐ 1 cup fat-free milk or low-fat, calcium-enriched soy or rice beverage

SNACK

☐ 1 medium orange or tangerine

☐ 2 tablespoons unsalted dry-roasted almonds (about 12)

DINNER

☐ 3 ounces chicken breast, grilled or roasted, with 2 tablespoons barbecue sauce

☐ 2 slices sourdough bread each spread with 1 teaspoon olive oil and minced garlic to taste and toasted

☐ Colorful Coleslaw: Mix 1 cup shredded red and green cabbage and carrots with 2 tablespoons reduced-fat (or 1 tablespoon regular) coleslaw dressing.

SNACK

☐ 3 squares graham crackers (1½ sheets)

☐ 1 tablespoon all-natural peanut butter

HOW DID YOU DO?

BALANCE YOUR BLOOD SUGAR

	TIME	READING
CHECK 1		
CHECK 2		
CHECK 3		
CHECK 4		
CHECK 5		

MEASURE YOURSELF

Week 2 weight: _____ pounds

> Winning isn't everything, but wanting to win is.
> —VINCE LOMBARDI

SUCCEED ALL DAY

Picture yourself fit. Every time a food you crave pops into your head, think, *Stop!* Then, focus on a healthy image—say, you, lean and fit, walking or running. After a while, your brain will dismiss the food image, and the craving will subside.

Ban work from the bedroom. If you pay bills, study, or work on your laptop in your bedroom, your brain associates this location with work rather than sleep. (Even crafts like scrapbooking are "work" to the brain.) Consider relocating your "office"—including your computer—to another room. Eventually, your brain will associate the bedroom only with sleep and sex if you use it only for those things.

DAY
9

1,400 CALORIES

BREAKFAST

❑ Fruit yogurt cup: Stir ¼ cup low-fat granola, 2 tablespoons flaxseed meal, and 1 tablespoon chopped unsalted raw nuts into 6 ounces no-sugar-added, fat-free flavored yogurt. Add ground cinnamon and/or sugar substitute to taste.

LUNCH

❑ Lean-Body Salad: Combine 2 cups mixed dark greens, ½ cup canned chickpeas, and 1 ounce shredded reduced-fat mozzarella cheese. Drizzle with 2 tablespoons light Italian dressing.

❑ 1 medium peach or ½ cup peaches canned in juice or water

SNACK

❑ 1 medium orange or 1 cup fresh strawberries

❑ 2 tablespoons unsalted raw nuts (almonds, peanuts, cashews, walnuts, pistachios)

DINNER

❑ 3 ounces lean roast beef

❑ 2 cups raw or 1 cup cooked spinach tossed with 1 teaspoon olive oil and 1 teaspoon balsamic vinegar

❑ ⅔ cup brown rice cooked with 1 teaspoon olive oil

SNACK

❑ 3 cups light microwave popcorn

❑ 1 ounce low-fat mozzarella string cheese

❑ 16 ounces light lemonade

1,600 CALORIES

BREAKFAST

❑ Fruit yogurt cup: Stir ¼ cup low-fat granola, 1 tablespoon flaxseed meal, and 2 tablespoons chopped unsalted raw nuts into 6 ounces no-sugar-added, fat-free flavored yogurt. Add ground cinnamon and/or sugar substitute to taste.

LUNCH

❑ Lean-Body Salad: Combine 1 ounce white-meat turkey or chicken with 2 cups mixed dark greens, ½ cup canned chickpeas, and 1 ounce shredded reduced-fat mozzarella cheese. Drizzle with 2 tablespoons light Italian dressing.

❑ 1 medium peach or ½ cup peaches canned in juice or water

SNACK

❑ 1 medium orange or 1 cup fresh strawberries

❑ ¼ cup unsalted raw nuts (almonds, peanuts, cashews, walnuts, pistachios)

DINNER

❑ 4 ounces lean roast beef

❑ 2 cups raw or 1 cup cooked spinach tossed with 1 teaspoon olive oil and 1 teaspoon balsamic vinegar

❑ ⅔ cup brown rice cooked with 1 teaspoon olive oil

SNACK

❑ 3 cups light microwave popcorn sprinkled with 2 tablespoons Romano cheese

❑ 16 ounces light lemonade

BALANCE YOUR BLOOD SUGAR

	TIME	READING
CHECK 1		
CHECK 2		
CHECK 3		
CHECK 4		
CHECK 5		

The significance of
a man is not in what
he attains but in what
he longs to attain.
—KAHLIL GIBRAN

SUCCEED ALL DAY

See the glass as half full. Optimists live longer than pessimists, according to a study of more than 1,100 people tracked for 30 years by the Mayo Clinic. In a separate study of 999 men and women ages 65 to 85, Dutch researchers found that optimistic participants were 77 percent less likely than the pessimists to die of cardiovascular diseases.

Time your last caffeine break. Avoid coffee, tea, and other caffeinated foods and drinks such as chocolate and colas for 6 to 8 hours before you turn in. Even if you don't think caffeine affects you, it could be disrupting the quality of your sleep: While caffeinated products remain in the body for an average of 3 to 5 hours, they can affect some people for up to 12 hours.

DAY
10

1,400 CALORIES

BREAKFAST

❒ 1 egg scrambled in 1 teaspoon canola or olive oil and topped with ½ cup salsa

❒ 1 whole grain English muffin, toasted and spread with 2 tablespoons 1% cottage cheese

❒ 1 cup fat-free milk or low-fat, calcium-enriched soy or rice beverage

LUNCH

❒ Chicken salad: Top 2 cups dark greens with 2 ounces cooked chicken breast; 2 stalks celery, chopped; and ¼ cup sliced grapes. Drizzle with 2 tablespoons light honey mustard dressing (such as Newman's Own).

❒ 1 slice reduced-calorie whole grain bread

❒ 1 teaspoon trans-free canola margarine

SNACK

❒ 1 cup watermelon (or other melon)

❒ 6 ounces no-sugar-added, fat-free or low-fat flavored yogurt

❒ 1 tablespoon dry-roasted mixed nuts

DINNER

❒ Preheat oven to 350°F. Place 4 ounces fresh halibut or other fish (4 ounces raw equals 3 ounces cooked) onto square piece of foil. Top with 1 cup chopped bell peppers and onions. Add salt-free seasoning (such as Mrs. Dash), garlic powder, lemon juice, and pepper. Wrap and bake for 20 to 30 minutes or until the fish flakes easily.

❒ Toss ½ cup sliced or diced red potatoes in 1 tablespoon olive oil. Place on cookie sheet and season with garlic, onion, or a salt-free seasoning (such as Mrs. Dash). Bake at 350°F for 30 to 45 minutes or until browned.

SNACK

❒ ¼ cup unsalted raw cashews, almonds, walnuts, or other nuts

1,600 CALORIES

BREAKFAST

❒ 1 egg scrambled in 1 teaspoon canola or olive oil and topped with ¼ cup salsa

❒ 1 whole grain English muffin, toasted and spread with 3 tablespoons 1% cottage cheese

❒ 1 cup fat-free milk or low-fat, calcium-enriched soy or rice beverage

LUNCH

❒ Chicken salad: Top 2 cups dark greens with 2 ounces cooked chicken breast; 2 stalks celery, chopped; and ¼ cup sliced grapes. Drizzle with 2 tablespoons light honey mustard dressing (such as Newman's Own).

❒ 2 slices reduced-calorie whole grain bread

❒ 2 teaspoons trans-free canola margarine

SNACK

❒ 1 cup watermelon (or other melon) chunks

❒ 6 ounces no-sugar-added, fat-free or low-fat flavored yogurt

❒ 2 tablespoons dry-roasted mixed nuts

DINNER

❒ Preheat oven to 350°F. Place 4 ounces fresh halibut or other fish (4 ounces raw equals 3 ounces cooked) onto square piece of foil. Top with 1 cup chopped bell peppers and onions. Add salt-free seasoning (such as Mrs. Dash), garlic powder, lemon juice, and pepper. Wrap and bake for 20 to 30 minutes or until the fish flakes easily.

❒ Toss 1 cup sliced or diced red potatoes in 1 tablespoon olive oil. Place on cookie sheet and season with garlic, onion, or a salt-free seasoning (such as Mrs. Dash). Bake at 350°F for 30 to 45 minutes or until browned.

SNACK

❒ ¼ cup unsalted raw cashews, almonds, walnuts, or other nuts

HOW DID YOU DO?

BALANCE YOUR BLOOD SUGAR

	TIME	READING
CHECK 1		
CHECK 2		
CHECK 3		
CHECK 4		
CHECK 5		

If you don't know
where you are going,
you might wind up
someplace else.
—YOGI BERRA

SUCCEED ALL DAY

Lead yourself not into temptation. If you're feeling shaky about your willpower, avoid locations and anything else that might trigger cravings, from cooking or food programs on TV to the snack aisles of supermarkets or convenience stores.

Reflect on your values. Going through a rough patch? Taking time to reflect on and affirm your personal values can help you cope. Researchers had 85 people undertake either a values-affirming task or a neutral task before undergoing a stressful lab test. Those who had affirmed their values released less cortisol, a stress hormone, than members of the control group did.

DAY 11

1,400 CALORIES

BREAKFAST

❐ Good-Morning Blend: Stir 2 tablespoons mixed dried fruits, 2 tablespoons flaxseed meal, and 2 tablespoons chopped unsalted raw almonds, walnuts, or pecans into 6 ounces no-sugar-added, fat-free flavored yogurt.

LUNCH

❐ Roast beef sandwich: Spread 1 teaspoon regular mayonnaise and 1 teaspoon mustard on 2 slices reduced-calorie whole grain bread or toast. Add 2 ounces lean roast beef. Top with $1/2$ cup chopped romaine lettuce and $1/2$ tomato, sliced.

SNACK

❐ 4 dried apricot halves or 3 dried plums (prunes)

❐ 7 walnut halves

DINNER

❐ $2/3$ cup cooked whole grain pasta tossed in 1 teaspoon olive oil and minced garlic to taste

❐ 3 ounces (about 5) lean turkey, chicken, or soy meatballs (such as Tyson Fully Cooked Italian Meatballs)

❐ 1 teaspoon grated Parmesan cheese

❐ Cucumber salad: On a bed of 1 cup mixed greens, arrange 1 cup cucumber slices, 10 halved cherry tomatoes, and $1/4$ cup chopped red onion. Drizzle with 1 tablespoon light Italian dressing.

SNACK

❐ 1 cup fat-free milk or low-fat, calcium-enriched soy or rice beverage

❐ 5 vanilla wafers or 3 graham cracker squares

1,600 CALORIES

BREAKFAST

❐ Good-Morning Blend: Stir 2 tablespoons mixed dried fruits, 2 tablespoons flaxseed meal, and 3 tablespoons chopped unsalted raw almonds, walnuts, or pecans into 6 ounces no-sugar-added, fat-free flavored yogurt.

LUNCH

❐ Roast beef sandwich: Spread 1 teaspoon regular mayonnaise and 1 teaspoon mustard on 2 slices reduced-calorie whole grain bread or toast. Add 4 ounces lean roast beef. Top with $1/2$ cup chopped romaine lettuce and $1/2$ tomato, sliced.

SNACK

❐ 4 dried apricot halves or 3 dried plums (prunes)

❐ 7 walnut halves

DINNER

❐ $3/4$ cup cooked whole grain pasta tossed in 2 teaspoons olive oil and minced garlic to taste

❐ 4 ounces (about 6) lean turkey, chicken, or soy meatballs (such as Tyson Fully Cooked Italian Meatballs)

❐ 2 teaspoons grated Parmesan cheese

❐ Cucumber salad: On a bed of 1 cup mixed greens, arrange 1 cup cucumber slices, 10 halved cherry tomatoes, and $1/4$ cup chopped red onion. Drizzle with 1 tablespoon light Italian dressing.

SNACK

❐ 1 cup fat-free milk or low-fat, calcium-enriched soy or rice beverage

❐ 5 vanilla wafers or 3 graham cracker squares

HOW DID YOU DO?

BALANCE YOUR BLOOD SUGAR

	TIME	READING
CHECK 1		
CHECK 2		
CHECK 3		
CHECK 4		
CHECK 5		

SUCCEED ALL DAY

Portion out a serving. If you can't beat a food craving, try this trick: Before you dig in, dole out a small amount of the food on a small plate. Then put the rest away.

Log off and tune out an hour before bed. The light from a TV or computer monitor mimics the intensity of sunlight, which fools your brain and body into thinking it's *not* time to sleep.

The thing always happens that you really believe in; and the belief in a thing makes it happen.
—FRANK LLOYD WRIGHT

DAY 12

1,400 CALORIES

BREAKFAST

☐ ½ cup cooked oatmeal or 1 cup whole oat cereal (such as Cheerios) topped with ¼ cup unsalted raw walnuts or other nuts. Add ½ teaspoon ground cinnamon and/or 1 teaspoon sugar substitute.

☐ 1 cup fat-free milk or low-fat, calcium-enriched soy or rice beverage

LUNCH

☐ Pesto pizza: Split and toast a whole grain English muffin. Spread with 1 tablespoon basil pesto sauce or ½ teaspoon olive oil seasoned with fresh basil. Top each half with 1 slice reduced-fat cheese and 1 slice tomato or 1 tablespoon canned tomatoes, drained. Broil or bake at 450°F until cheese melts.

SNACK

☐ 2 fresh or dried figs

☐ 12 almonds or ½ ounce other nuts

DINNER

☐ Shrimp salad bowl: Mix together ⅓ cup cooked brown rice and 2 tablespoons crumbled feta cheese. Arrange on 2 cups mixed greens. Top with 3 ounces grilled or sautéed shrimp or other fish. Drizzle with 2 tablespoons light Italian dressing.

☐ 2 rye crisp crackers spread with 2 tablespoons low-fat ricotta or 1% cottage cheese

SNACK

☐ 6 ounces no-sugar-added, fat-free or low-fat flavored yogurt

☐ 1 medium orange *or* ¾ cup blueberries, raspberries, or blackberries

1,600 CALORIES

BREAKFAST

☐ 1 cup cooked oatmeal or 1 cup whole oat cereal (such as Cheerios) topped with ¼ cup unsalted raw walnuts or other nuts. Add ½ teaspoon ground cinnamon and/or 1 teaspoon sugar substitute to taste.

☐ 1 cup fat-free milk or low-fat, calcium-enriched soy or rice beverage

LUNCH

☐ Pesto pizza: Split and toast a whole grain English muffin. Spread with 2 tablespoons basil pesto sauce or 1 teaspoon olive oil seasoned with fresh basil. Top each half with 1 slice reduced-fat cheese and 1 slice tomato or 1 tablespoon canned tomatoes, drained. Broil or bake at 450°F until cheese melts.

SNACK

☐ 2 fresh or dried figs

☐ 12 almonds or ½ ounce other nuts

DINNER

☐ Shrimp salad bowl: Mix together ½ cup cooked brown rice and 2 tablespoons crumbled feta cheese. Arrange on 2 cups mixed greens. Top with 4 ounces grilled or sautéed shrimp or other fish. Drizzle with 2 tablespoons light Italian dressing.

☐ 2 rye crisp crackers spread with 3 tablespoons low-fat ricotta or 1% cottage cheese

SNACK

☐ 6 ounces no-sugar-added, fat-free or low-fat flavored yogurt

☐ 1 medium orange *or* ¾ cup blueberries, raspberries, or blackberries

HOW DID YOU DO?

BALANCE YOUR BLOOD SUGAR

	TIME	READING
CHECK 1		
CHECK 2		
CHECK 3		
CHECK 4		
CHECK 5		

SUCCEED ALL DAY

Know thy stressors. When you perceive that you're not in control, levels of stress hormones rise. Devise solutions to "uncontrollable" sources of stress (a long commute, your partner's sloppiness) to help defuse them. **Prepare your bladder for bed.** If middle-of-the-night bathroom visits routinely disrupt your slumber, be proactive. Make it a habit to empty your bladder before you turn in, and don't drink more than 4 ounces of fluids within an hour of bedtime.

If you don't like something, change it. If you can't change it, change your attitude. Don't complain.
—MAYA ANGELOU

1,400 CALORIES

BREAKFAST

- ❏ ½ whole grain bagel spread with 1 tablespoon low-fat cream cheese
- ❏ 1 cup fat-free milk or low-fat, calcium-enriched soy or rice beverage

LUNCH

- ❏ Bean tostada: Preheat oven to 400°F. Bake 1 corn tortilla (6-inch diameter) until crisp (about 5 to 10 minutes). Spread with ½ cup cooked pinto beans and 2 tablespoons shredded reduced-fat Mexican-blend cheese. Return tortilla to oven for 5 to 10 minutes until cheese melts, or microwave on medium power for 30 to 45 seconds. Top with ¼ cup salsa.
- ❏ Cabbage salad: Combine 1 cup shredded cabbage with 1 tomato, chopped, and drizzle with 2 tablespoons light ranch or creamy Italian dressing.

SNACK

- ❏ 1 kiwi or small orange
- ❏ 12 whole almonds

DINNER

- ❏ Oven-fried chicken: Preheat oven to 350°F. Toss 4 ounces raw chicken breast in 1 tablespoon light Italian dressing. Coat with 2 tablespoons seasoned bread crumbs and spray lightly with canola oil spray. Place chicken on a lightly oiled cookie sheet. Bake for 30 minutes, or until browned on the outside and no longer pink inside.
- ❏ 3-bean salad: Toss ½ cup cooked green beans, ¼ cup cooked chickpeas, ¼ cup cooked red beans, and 2 tablespoons chopped onion with 2 tablespoons light Italian dressing.

SNACK

- ❏ ½ cup light ice cream
- ❏ 1 tablespoon chopped walnuts

1,600 CALORIES

BREAKFAST

- ❏ ½ whole grain bagel spread with 2 tablespoons low-fat cream cheese and 2 ounces lox (smoked salmon)
- ❏ 1 cup fat-free milk or low-fat, calcium-enriched soy or rice beverage

LUNCH

- ❏ Bean tostadas: Preheat oven to 400°F. Bake 2 corn tortillas (6-inch diameter) until crisp (about 5 to 10 minutes). Spread with ½ cup cooked pinto beans and 2 tablespoons shredded reduced-fat Mexican-blend cheese. Return tortillas to oven for 5 to 10 minutes until cheese melts, or microwave on medium power for 30 to 45 seconds. Top with ¼ cup salsa.
- ❏ Cabbage salad: Combine 1 cup shredded cabbage with 1 tomato, chopped, and drizzle with 2 tablespoons light ranch or creamy Italian dressing.

SNACK

- ❏ 1 kiwi or small orange
- ❏ 1 ounce whole almonds (about 23)

DINNER

- ❏ Oven-fried chicken: Preheat oven to 350°F. Toss 5 ounces raw chicken breast in 1 tablespoon light Italian dressing. Coat with 2 tablespoons seasoned bread crumbs and spray lightly with canola oil spray. Place chicken on lightly oiled cookie sheet. Bake for 30 minutes, or until browned on the outside and no longer pink inside.
- ❏ 3-bean salad: Toss ½ cup cooked green beans, ¼ cup cooked chickpeas, ¼ cup cooked red beans, and 2 tablespoons chopped onion with 2 tablespoons light Italian dressing.

SNACK

- ❏ ½ cup light ice cream
- ❏ 1 tablespoon chopped walnuts

HOW DID YOU DO?

BALANCE YOUR BLOOD SUGAR

	TIME	READING
CHECK 1		
CHECK 2		
CHECK 3		
CHECK 4		
CHECK 5		

To climb steep hills
requires slow pace
at first.
—SHAKESPEARE

SUCCEED ALL DAY

Keep a stash of Tootsie Rolls. They're sweet. They're chewy. They're chocolaty good. Best of all, these tiny treats will quash a chocolate craving for fewer calories and less fat. What's not to love?

Swap the bubbly for a bubble bath. If you tend to "relax" with alcohol, swap it for some of the tension tamers in this book. Abusing alcohol raises levels of triglycerides and can lead to high blood pressure and heart failure.

1,400 CALORIES

BREAKFAST

❒ Veggie omelet: Heat 1 teaspoon canola, peanut, or olive oil in a skillet. Add ½ cup egg substitute (or 1 egg white); 1 cup spinach leaves; ½ cup chopped mushrooms, onion, and garlic; and herbs as desired. Cook over low heat until set. Top with 2 tablespoons shredded reduced-fat cheese.

❒ 1 slice whole grain toast spread with 1 teaspoon trans-free canola margarine

❒ 1 cup fat-free milk or low-fat, calcium-enriched soy or rice beverage

LUNCH

❒ Tuna salad: Mix 3 ounces water-packed tuna, drained, with 2 stalks celery, chopped; 4 green olives, chopped; and 1 tablespoon reduced-fat mayonnaise (or 1 teaspoon regular mayonnaise). Add 1 tablespoon seasoned rice vinegar, if desired. Serve on a bed of 2 cups mixed dark greens. Top with 1 tablespoon chopped unsalted raw almonds.

❒ 3 slices whole grain crispbread (such as Wasa crackers)

SNACK

❒ 1 medium apple, sliced

❒ 2 tablespoons all-natural peanut butter

DINNER

❒ Tofu stir-fry: Stir-fry 3 ounces firm tofu (processed with calcium sulfate) and 2 cups mixed vegetables (broccoli, cauliflower, green beans, onion) in 2 tablespoons reduced-sodium stir-fry sauce and 1 tablespoon olive oil. Serve over ⅓ cup cooked brown or wild rice.

SNACK

❒ Stir 1 tablespoon chopped dried fruits and 1 tablespoon chopped unsalted raw nuts into 6 ounces no-sugar-added, fat-free flavored yogurt.

1,600 CALORIES

BREAKFAST

❒ Veggie omelet: Heat 2 teaspoons canola, peanut, or olive oil in a skillet. Add ½ cup egg substitute (or 1 egg white); ½ cup spinach leaves; ½ cup chopped mushrooms, onion, and garlic; and herbs as desired. Cook over low heat until set. Top with 2 tablespoons shredded reduced-fat cheese.

❒ 1 slice whole grain toast spread with 2 teaspoons trans-free canola margarine

❒ 1 cup fat-free milk or low-fat, calcium-enriched soy or rice beverage

LUNCH

❒ Tuna salad: Mix 3 ounces water-packed tuna, drained, with 2 stalks celery, chopped; 4 green olives, chopped; and 1 tablespoon reduced-fat mayonnaise (or 1 teaspoon regular mayonnaise). Add 1 tablespoon seasoned rice vinegar, if desired. Serve on 2 cups mixed dark greens. Top with 1 tablespoon chopped unsalted raw almonds.

❒ 3 slices whole grain crispbread (such as Wasa crackers)

SNACK

❒ 1 medium apple, sliced

❒ 2 tablespoons all-natural peanut butter

DINNER

❒ Tofu stir-fry: Stir-fry 4 ounces firm tofu (processed with calcium sulfate) and 2 cups mixed vegetables (broccoli, cauliflower, green beans, onion) in 2 tablespoons reduced-sodium stir-fry sauce and 1 tablespoon olive oil. Serve over ⅓ cup cooked brown or wild rice.

SNACK

❒ Stir 1 tablespoon chopped dried fruits and 1 tablespoon chopped unsalted raw nuts into 6 ounces no-sugar-added, fat-free flavored yogurt.

HOW DID YOU DO?

BALANCE YOUR BLOOD SUGAR

	TIME	READING
CHECK 1		
CHECK 2		
CHECK 3		
CHECK 4		
CHECK 5		

Keep steadily before you the fact that all true success depends at last upon yourself.
—THEODORE T. HUNGER

SUCCEED ALL DAY

Have a bit of the best. If you're a chocolate connoisseur, you might feel that chocolate imitations are unacceptable. Get your fix of the good stuff in small (150-calorie) doses. That's two truffles or one snack-size bar.

Leave worries in the dark. If you're tossing and turning, get up and go to another part of the house, but leave the lights off. Usually, anxious thoughts will stop right away, so you can return to bed and fall asleep. This strategy, called stimulus control, also prevents you from associating your bed with anxiety.

TRANSFORMATION TOOL #1: GET FIT

Some experts describe exercise as medicine without the pill. Name any chronic health problem, and exercise probably can help control it, if not reverse it. Type 2 diabetes is a perfect example. Time and again, research has shown that regular physical activity helps lower blood sugar because the body uses insulin more efficiently. In fact, people with type 2 who are taking medication are often able to reduce their dosages. Likewise, those who have type 2 but aren't taking medication may not need it quite so soon, if at all.

We designed the DTOUR Workout in consultation with diabetes and fitness experts, in addition to using the very latest research. The workout is basic—short, easy-to-remember routines; simple moves; and no gym visits or pricey gear. It's enjoyable because *you* get to define *enjoyable*. It's also customizable; you can adjust it to your changing health and fitness level, as well as to the demands of your schedule. And best of all, it *works*.

The DTOUR Workout Blocks

Using the DARE findings as our main point of reference, we designed the DTOUR Workout to target a trio of fitness benchmarks: cardiorespiratory fitness (which reflects how well the heart and lungs supply oxygen to the muscles during exercise), muscular strength and endurance, and flexibility. Now, don't break into a sweat just yet; as with all things DTOUR, we're going to make exercise as accessible and doable as we can. In fact, the workout consists of four building blocks—two aerobic, two strength and flexibility—that you interchange. It's really that easy!

What follows is a short description of each of the four blocks. We'll explore each block in more detail in just a bit. The 4-Week Total Transformation, which begins on page 82, spells out each day's workout for you.

Before we go further, we want to stress the importance of following the DTOUR Workout at your own pace. Your fitness level is going to improve over time, so there's no need to do too much too soon. Also, get your doctor's clearance before starting any fitness routine, especially if you have diabetes. Exercise will affect your blood sugar, so it's smart to proceed with care.

BLOCKS A AND B: THE CARDIO WALKS

Brisk walking is an ideal form of aerobic exercise—it's convenient, it's low impact, and it requires no special equipment other than a good pair of walking shoes.

The DTOUR Workout features two Cardio Walks.

◆ For the Fat-Torch Walk (Block A), you'll maintain a steady, moderate-intensity pace from beginning to end. Research has shown that this style of walking helps to burn body fat. The Fat-Torch walk is slightly longer than the Calorie-Scorch Walk, making it more challenging.

◆ The Calorie-Scorch Walk (Block B) combines a moderate-intensity pace with *intervals*—that is, short bursts of fast walking. Interval training keeps your metabolism in high gear for hours after you finish a workout, so you burn more calories throughout the day.

We suggest starting out with 1 minute at moderate intensity, followed by 30 seconds at vigorous intensity; then continue switching between the two. As you become more fit, you can increase to 1 minute at moderate intensity and 1-minute intervals. Remember to allow 3 minutes for warming up at the beginning of our workout, and 2 minutes for cooling down at the end.

For the 6 weeks of the Total Transformation, you'll be doing the Cardio Walks 4 to 6 days a week. As your fitness improves, so will the duration of your walks. Your pace will pick up, too—and the faster you move, the more calories you use.

BLOCK C: THE METABO MOVES

This mini-but-mighty strength-training routine delivers a multitude of benefits.

◆ It firms and tones your upper and lower body in just four moves (and one optional move). You can modify each move to make it more or less challenging. Do the version of each move that matches your fitness level.

◆ Strength training builds muscle, which burns more calories than fat does. So the more muscle you have, the more calories you burn, even in your sleep. (Sweet!)

◆ The more muscle you have, the more sensitive to insulin you become. Some studies suggest that strength training enhances cells' insulin response and improves blood sugar just as effectively as diabetes medication does.

◆ As a bonus, strength training is the sort of weight-bearing activity that builds bone density and helps protect against the bone-thinning disease osteoporosis.

You'll perform the Metabo Moves 2 or 3 days a week.

BLOCK D: THE BELLY BLAST

The four moves in this strength-and-flexibility routine zero in on the muscles of your core—that is, the abdominals, lower back, hips, and buttocks. You'll sculpt a tight, trim torso without doing a single crunch! Plus, you'll be targeting belly fat, the kind that contributes to insulin resistance and is a risk factor for metabolic syndrome.

You'll be doing the Belly Blast 2 or 3 days a week. As with the Metabo Moves, you can adjust each move to your fitness level.

THE DTOUR WORKOUT BASICS

DTOUR makes fitness easy, accessible, and fun! With the combination of aerobic exercise and strength training in this plan, you'll burn calories, melt away fat–and lower your blood sugar, to boot. The 4-Week Total Transformation spells out each day's workout for you; use the guidelines here to get the most from your exercise minutes.

◆ Get your doctor's okay *before* you begin any exercise program.
◆ Perform all workouts at your own pace.
◆ Warm up for 3 minutes before every Cardio Walk, and cool down for 2 minutes afterward. Include these 5 minutes in your total workout time. As for how to warm up and cool down, you needn't do anything elaborate; you might walk at a slower pace or simply march in place.
◆ Do Cardio Walks 4 to 6 times a week.
◆ Do the Metabo Moves and Belly Blast 2 or 3 times a week. The moves in each routine can be modified to increase or reduce the challenge. Choose the version of each move that matches your fitness level.
◆ You may do either the Metabo Moves or the Belly Blast on the same day as a Cardio Walk.
◆ You may do the Metabo Moves and the Belly Blast on the same day. Be sure to allow 1 rest day before your next strength-training session.
◆ Rest at least 1 day each week.

Mastering the Cardio Walks

It's important to learn and maintain good form for your Cardio Walks—not only to maximize your calorie burn, but also to avoid injury. Here's a head-to-toe guide to proper walking technique.

♦ **Head, shoulders, and chest:** Hold your head high, so your neck and the rest of your spine form a straight line. Your chin should be level with the ground; avoid tucking it in toward your neck. Raise your chest and relax your shoulders. An easy way to check your shoulder position on the fly: Take a deep breath every 5 minutes, then exhale strongly. Notice how your shoulders drop? That's how you want to carry them.

♦ **Eyes:** Look well ahead of you—anywhere from 10 to 30 feet, experts say.

♦ **Arms and hands:** Bend your elbows to 90-degree angles and keep them close to your sides. They should move to the rear, but not outward, as you walk. Imagine a shelf extending from your chest and try not to let your hands shoot above it.

♦ **Abdominals and hips:** Your abdominal muscles should be tight. Pull your belly button toward your spine and tuck your pelvis slightly forward. Power your movement from your glutes (that is, your butt) rather than your thighs; let your hips swing.

♦ **Legs:** Taking huge strides actually slows you down. To determine the natural length of your stride, stand straight and extend one foot a few inches in front of you, with your leg straight and your heel not quite touching the ground. Then slowly lean forward; don't worry—your extended heel will hit the ground and stop you from falling. That's how far forward your front foot should go during your stride. (For this test, don't pay attention to the position of your back leg. When you're walking, your back leg will be farther behind you.)

♦ **Feet:** When you step forward, your heel should gently strike the ground before your foot rolls forward and allows you to push off from your toes. Make sure you aren't pounding your feet; if you are, you're not channeling enough energy forward, so you're decreasing your momentum.

It's best to stretch a few minutes into your walk, when your muscles are warm, rather than before you start.

GOT DIABETES? BE SMART ABOUT WORKING OUT

There's no doubt that exercise can be a real asset in managing diabetes. It stabilizes blood sugar not only by helping cells use insulin more effectively, but also by burning off excess body fat, which further improves insulin response.

If you have diabetes, you need to be somewhat choosy about how much exercise you get and what kinds. Some activities may not be right for you, especially if you're experiencing complications such as heart disease, kidney disease, or eye or foot problems.

Your doctor can start you on the right path by reviewing the DTOUR Workout with you and suggesting adjustments based on your health status and fitness level. The following pointers can help, too.

If you have diabetes-related eye problems: Too-heavy weights can increase the pressure in the blood vessels of your eyes. Ask your doctor how much you can safely lift.

If nerve damage has made your feet numb: You may want to choose an aerobic activity other than walking, such as bicycling or swimming. Discuss the options with your doctor. If he or she gives you the all-clear to do the Cardio Walks, be sure to wear shoes that fit. And check your feet for any sores, bumps, or redness after every workout.

If you take a diabetes medication that can cause low blood sugar: You may need to adjust your dosage before your workout, or eat a snack if your blood sugar is below 100. Ask your doctor what's best for you.

After your workout: Check your blood sugar. If it's below 70, have *one* of the following immediately:

◆ 3 or 4 glucose tablets *or* 1 serving glucose gel (15 grams carbohydrate)
◆ ½ cup fruit juice
◆ 5 or 6 pieces hard candy
◆ 1 tablespoon sugar or honey

After 15 minutes, check your blood sugar again. If it's still low, go back for another "dose." Repeat until your blood sugar is 70 or higher.

Mastering the Metabo Moves

For the Metabo Moves, you'll need two pieces of gear: a set of dumbbells (ideally of varying weights) and an exercise mat. You'll be doing this routine 2 or 3 times a week.

The following tips will help guide you through your routine so you'll be doing the moves safely and effectively. Within about a month, you'll notice changes in your body as you replace fat with muscle. Other changes—including a huge surge in energy and an overall improvement in your mood—will happen much sooner. (If you're working with weights for the first time, be sure to get the all-clear from your doctor before diving in.)

◆ A *repetition* (or *rep*, for short) describes 1 complete exercise. A *set* is a specific number of repetitions. Do 2 sets of 8 to 12 repetitions of each exercise. Start with 8 repetitions per set. When you can easily do 12 reps, use a heavier dumbbell.

◆ Choose the right weight. If you can't lift a dumbbell 8 times while maintaining good form, it's too heavy. On the other hand, it's too light if you can easily lift it more than 12 times. Pick a weight that's in between.

◆ Be careful not to hold your breath when you lift, because it can cause your blood pressure to spike. Practice exhaling as you lift the weight, then inhaling as you lower it or return to the starting position.

◆ Perform each move in a slow, controlled manner to help prevent injury. It should take 3 seconds to lift the weight into place and another 3 to return to the starting position, with a 1-second pause in between. Bonus: Because slowly lifting a dumbbell requires more effort, you get more benefit.

◆ Doing the Metabo Moves in precisely the right way—pros call this *good form*—helps you get the most benefit from lifting while avoiding injury. Until you're familiar with the routine, you might want to practice it while standing in front of a mirror so you can monitor your posture and movement. You can use the photos beginning on page 60 for reference. Another option: Sign up for a session with a personal trainer, who can observe and correct your form.

◆ That said, don't get so hung up on form that you're petrified to even attempt the moves. Just be patient and work slowly, in a mindful way.

◆ Rest your muscles for at least 1 day between workouts. It's during rest that your muscles grow. Lifting weights causes tiny tears in muscle tissue; as your muscles repair this damage, they become stronger.

◆ You may feel a little sore for a week or so after you begin strength training. That's normal. If you experience outright pain, however, you may be overdoing it. Stop and rest for a day or two before trying again.

THE METABO MOVES

1. PENDULUM KICKBACK

Tones the triceps, butt, and thighs.

Holding a dumbbell in each hand, stand with your left leg straight in front of you. Your foot should be flexed and about 6 to 12 inches off the floor. Bend your elbows to 90-degree angles so your forearms are parallel to the floor. Swing your left leg behind you, and squeeze your glutes as you straighten your arms. Return to the starting position, then repeat for a full set before switching legs.

2. CROUCH AND PULL
Tones the shoulders, upper back, arms, obliques, butt, and thighs.
Holding a dumbbell in each hand, stand with your feet about shoulder-width apart and sit back into a partial squat. Hinge forward from your hips about 45 degrees, keeping your arms extended below your shoulders and your palms facing in. With your lower body facing forward, rotate your torso to the left. Bend your left arm and pull the dumbbell toward your chest, pointing your elbow toward the ceiling. Return to the starting position, then repeat, alternating sides. Do 2 full sets per side.

Simplify it: If you have back problems, use one weight at a time and place the other hand on a chair for support.

A

3. KNEE-HUGGER CHEST FLY
Tones the chest and abs.
Holding a dumbbell in each hand, lie faceup on an exercise mat with your knees bent and your shins parallel to the floor. Your arms should be out to your sides, with your elbows slightly bent and your palms facing the ceiling. Contract your abdominal muscles and lift your hips about 3 inches off the floor. At the same time, squeeze your chest muscles and raise your arms, bringing the dumbbells together over your chest. Lower your hips and arms to the starting position, then repeat.

B

4. FIGURE-4 SQUAT CURL
Tones the biceps, butt, and thighs. Hold a dumbbell in your left hand at your side, with your palm facing forward. Cross your right ankle over your left thigh (A). Bend your left knee and hip and sit back, keeping your knee behind your toes; as you do, raise the dumbbell to your left shoulder (B). Return to the starting position. Repeat for a full set before switching sides.
Simplify it: Hold on to the back of a chair as shown.

OPTIONAL:
LIFTOFF LUNGE
**Tones the shoulders,
triceps, butt, and thighs.**

Stand with your feet hip-width apart. Hold both dumbbells at your shoulders, with your palms facing forward. Step back about 2 feet with your right foot, then bend both knees and lower yourself until your left thigh is about parallel to the floor, keeping your knee over your ankle. Press into your left foot and stand up as you pull your right knee forward so you're balancing on your left leg. Raise the weights overhead. Then, without touching the floor, swing your right leg back into the lunge position as you lower the weights. Repeat for a full set before switching legs.

Mastering the Belly Blast

The Belly Blast requires no equipment other than an exercise mat. You'll be doing this routine 2 or 3 times a week. As is the case for the Metabo Moves, maintaining good form is crucial. These tips can help.

◆ For maximum results, flatten your belly by pulling your navel toward your spine during each rep.

◆ Focus on keeping your abdominal muscles pulled in and up at all times.

◆ Work slowly and with precision to gain the maximum benefit from each move.

◆ Breathe in through your nose and out through your mouth. This deep inhaling and exhaling rids your lungs of stale air and fills them with fresh, oxygen-rich air, which energizes your entire body.

THE BELLY BLAST

1. TOE DIP
Lie on your back with your feet off the floor and your knees bent (A). Your thighs should be straight up and your calves parallel to the floor. Rest your hands at your sides, with your palms facing down. Contract your abs and press your lower back toward the floor. Inhale and lower your left leg for a count of 2, moving only from your hip (B). Your toes should dip toward the floor without actually touching it. Exhale and raise your leg to the starting position for a count of 2. Repeat with your right leg, then continue alternating until you've done 12 reps with each leg.

2. LEG CIRCLE

Lie on your back with your legs straight and extended along the floor. Your hands should be at your sides, palms facing down. Raise your right leg toward the ceiling, pointing your toes as you do. Hold for 10 to 60 seconds.

Rotate your right leg from the hip and make a small circle on the ceiling with the toes of your right foot. Inhale as you begin the circle and exhale as you finish.

Keep your body as still as possible by tightening your abs. Do 6 circles in one direction, then reverse direction for 6 more. Return to the starting position, then repeat with your left leg.

Simplify it: If keeping one leg flat on the floor is uncomfortable, try bending that leg and placing your foot flat on the floor.

A

B

3. CRISSCROSS

For this move, the starting position is the same as for the Toe Dip, only your hands are behind your head and your elbows are out to the sides (A). Curl up to raise your head, neck, and shoulders off the floor.

As you inhale, rotate your torso to the right, bringing your right knee and left shoulder toward each other and extending your left leg toward the ceiling in a diagonal line from your hip (B). As you exhale, rotate to the left, bringing your left knee and right shoulder toward each other and extending your right leg. That's 1 rep. Do 5 more, for a total of 6.

4. LEG KICK

Lie on your right side with your legs straight and together, so your body forms one long line. Prop yourself up on your right elbow and forearm, lifting your ribs off the floor and your head toward the ceiling. Place your left hand lightly on the floor in front of you for balance. Raise your left leg to hip level and flex your foot so your toes point forward.

Exhale as you kick, swinging your left leg forward as far as comfortably possible (A). Pulse for 2 counts (kick, kick). Inhale, point your toes, and swing your leg backward past your right leg (B). That's 1 rep. Do 6 reps without lowering your leg, then switch sides and repeat.

Simplify it: If propping yourself up on your elbow is uncomfortable, extend your right arm along the floor and rest your head on your arm.

THE DTOUR WORKOUT AT A GLANCE: WEEKS 1 TO 4

Include a 3-minute warmup and a 2-minute cooldown in the total time of your Cardio Walk.

	WEEK 1	WEEK 2	WEEK 3	WEEK 4
Day 1	Fat-Torch Walk, 20 minutes	Fat-Torch Walk, 25 minutes	Fat-Torch Walk, 30 minutes	Fat-Torch Walk, 35 minutes
Day 2	Metabo Moves; Belly Blast	Metabo Moves; Belly Blast	Calorie-Scorch Walk, 25 minutes	Calorie-Scorch Walk, 30 minutes
Day 3	Calorie-Scorch Walk, 15 minutes	Calorie-Scorch Walk, 20 minutes	Metabo Moves; Belly Blast	Metabo Moves; Belly Blast
Day 4	Rest day	Fat-Torch Walk, 25 minutes	Fat-Torch Walk, 30 minutes	Rest day
Day 5	Fat-Torch Walk, 20 minutes	Rest day	Rest day	Fat-Torch Walk, 35 minutes
Day 6	Metabo Moves; Belly Blast	Metabo Moves; Belly Blast	Calorie-Scorch Walk, 25 minutes	Calorie-Scorch Walk, 30 minutes
Day 7	Calorie-Scorch Walk, 15 minutes	Calorie-Scorch Walk, 20 minutes	Metabo Moves; Belly Blast	Metabo Moves; Belly Blast

PACE GUIDE FOR FAT-TORCH AND CALORIE-SCORCH CARDIO WALKS

This chart can help you gauge the speed and intensity of your Cardio Walks. Remember that what feels like a light workout to one person may be vigorous for another, so use the speeds as guides, not gospel.

	INTENSITY LEVEL	SPEED (MPH)
Warmup and cooldown	Light (you can sing)	3-3$\frac{1}{2}$
Fat-Torch Walk	Moderate (you can chat with a friend)	3$\frac{1}{2}$-4
Calorie-Scorch Walk, intervals only	Vigorous (you're edging slightly out of your comfort zone)	4+

TRANSFORMATION TOOL #2: SLEEP BETTER

If you're like most Americans, you probably aren't getting as much shut-eye as you should. This downtime is essential for your body to be able to repair damage and restore vital processes. Without it, your health can take a hit in unexpected ways.

Some of the most fascinating research findings of late have turned attention to the effects of sleep—or a lack of it—on weight gain and blood sugar control. Consider the results of a study from the National Center for Health Statistics, which from 2004 through 2006 surveyed 87,000 men and women about their sleep and related risk factors. The data revealed obesity to be most common among participants getting less than 6 hours of sleep a night. A full one-third of them—33 percent—were identified as obese, compared with just 22 percent of those getting between 7 and 8 hours of sleep each night.

Other studies point to a possible link between too little or poor-quality sleep and an increased risk of type 2 diabetes. One explanation for this comes from a 2007 study at the University of Chicago, in which researchers found that suppressing the deepest stage of sleep (called slow-wave sleep) interferes with the body's ability to regulate blood sugar.

So now you have even more reason to get a good night's sleep every night. That's why we've designated sleep as one of your Transformation Tools. Over the next 4 weeks of DTOUR, we'll be passing along lots of expert-recommended tips and techniques for making sure you get the optimal 7 to 8 hours, and that every one of those hours is restful and rejuvenating. Improved sleep translates into better weight and blood sugar control. Kind of gives new meaning to the term *sweet dreams*, doesn't it?

A Recipe for the Perfect Night's Sleep

The science certainly is impressive, but we'd venture to guess that you don't need a raft of studies to sell you on the health benefits of sleep. After all, you know how fabulous you feel when you get a full 7 to 8 hours of deep, undis-turbed slumber. The challenge is to do it consistently, night after night. You can, if you approach it in a systematic way.

We like to compare the process of creating a good night's sleep to that of making a new dish for the first time. To start, you probably follow the recipe to the letter to get the best results. Then, as you become comfortable with it, you tweak it to suit your and your family's tastes—always sticking with the basic recipe, but adding a pinch of this or a dash of that to make it "just right."

There's a basic recipe for sleep, too, and it comes from the National Sleep Foundation. Its staple ingredients are good sleep habits, which include the following:

◆ Use your bed only for sleep and sex.

◆ Try to turn in at the same time each night and get up at the same time each morning.

◆ Finish eating 2 to 3 hours before your regular bedtime.

◆ Exercise regularly, but end your workout at least 3 hours before bed-time. Otherwise, you could have a hard time falling asleep.

◆ Stop caffeinated foods (chocolate) and drinks (coffee, tea, diet cola) 6 to 8 hours before bedtime.

◆ Skip the nightcap before bedtime. Alcohol can interfere with sleep quality and cause you to wake up during the night.

◆ Establish a relaxing prebedtime routine. Taking a warm bath or sip-ping a cup of noncaffeinated herbal tea can help you wind down.

◆ Get into bed only when you're tired.

Once you have this recipe down pat, you can tinker with it by adding ingre-dients that help you create a peaceful, comfortable sleep environment. Things like noise, light (or, rather, darkness), and temperature are to sleep as salt and pepper are to cooking: simple, but vital to the outcome and thoroughly indi-vidual. Feel free to pick and choose from the following tips, as well as those offered throughout the 4-Week Total Transformation. Even one small change can have a big impact on your sleep experience—and that means better weight and blood sugar control.

NOISE

Some of us can sleep through a dripping faucet or the neighbor's barking dog; others wake up at the slightest bump or creak. Some of us need the *whoosh* of a fan to help us nod off; for others, only the familiar screech of sirens or rumble of trains will do the trick.

The point is, each of us has a unique noise threshold that plays an important role in determining how quickly we fall asleep and whether we stay asleep. Experiment with these strategies to find your personal lullaby.

Make some (white) noise. If you combine all of the sound frequencies that are audible to humans (there are about 20,000), you hear the soft hiss of what's called *white noise*. Because white noise contains all frequencies, it masks other sounds.

To make your own white noise, just turn on a fan or air conditioner. It will block out any sounds that disturb you—or fill the silence that keeps you awake. If you prefer something more high-tech, invest in a white-noise machine, also known as a *sound conditioner*. These gadgets come in all sizes and styles, but generally they can be programmed to produce either a sleep-promoting hiss or the soothing sounds of nature.

Install sound-absorbent accessories. Hang heavy curtains or drapes in your bedroom, or lay down thick carpet. Both of these absorb slumber-disturbing noises.

Travel with your favorite sleep sound. A small fan, a ticking clock, or a favorite CD can help you get your rest away from home.

Snore-proof your spouse. If your partner's snoring disrupts your sleep (not to mention your sanity), the two of you need to work out a compromise. It's not only your sleep that's at stake, but your partner's health, too. We'll talk more about this later.

LIGHT AND DARKNESS

Much of our sleep pattern (i.e., feeling awake during the day and sleepy at night) is regulated by light and darkness. As we awake each morning, the natural light entering our retinas sets our biological clocks for the day. Later on, nightfall prompts the release of melatonin, the hormone that promotes drowsiness and sleep.

Maintaining this cycle, known as circadian rhythm, is vital to sleep quantity and quality. You need to find just the right balance between light and darkness as you go about your daytime and bedtime routines. Here's how.

During the day, get some sun. Bright outdoor light is the most powerful regulator of your biological clock, the master timekeeper in your brain that determines when you feel alert and when you feel sleepy. So head outside for some direct sunlight; even 10 minutes a day will do the trick. (Remember, too, that your body uses sunlight to synthesize vitamin D, one of our all-important Fat-Fighting 4!)

At night, forgo bright overhead lights. Even 30 minutes of exposure to light that's slightly brighter than that in a typical office can suppress melatonin production. Instead, use task lamps with 40- to 60-watt incandescent bulbs when washing dishes, reading, or watching television.

At bedtime, go for blackout conditions. Try wearing an eye mask, or dress your bedroom windows with light-blocking curtains or drapes. If you use a night-light in your bedroom, equip it with a 7-watt incandescent bulb. It's okay to briefly turn on a low-wattage lightbulb for a bathroom run.

Shed light on middle-of-the-night wake-ups. If you typically awaken earlier than you'd like to, try increasing your exposure to bright light by an hour or two in the evening. It may take you longer to fall asleep, but you'll stay asleep longer in the morning.

TEMPERATURE

Many of us consider a cool, crisp night to be ideal "sleeping weather." Sleep researchers tend to agree. You see, about 4 hours after you fall asleep, your body temperature drops to its lowest daily level. So by keeping your bedroom on the cool side, you mimic your body's internal thermostat. And this, in turn, helps to regulate your body's cycle of alertness and fatigue.

While sleep researchers typically recommend keeping the bedroom between 60° and 70°F, it may take some getting used to—especially if your (or your partner's) internal thermostat runs hotter or colder. These tips can help keep you cozy and comfortable.

In cold weather: You can lock in the heat by using a thick comforter or an electric blanket. Or, wear warmer pajamas. Then, if you get too warm during the night, stick your foot out from under the covers. It's natural climate control!

In hot weather: Sleep is lighter and nighttime awakenings increase, research suggests. But closing the windows and running an air conditioner all night can cause your nose and throat to dry out, which could be just as uncomfortable. Here's a compromise: Use the air conditioner in tandem with a humidifier to moisten your nasal passages and throat.

In any climate: When you sit for most of the day, your core temperature remains low—and you stay wide awake at night when you're supposed to be sleepy. The DTOUR Workout, starting on page 54, is one surefire way to get moving, but even a brief walk can be beneficial. In one study involving more than 700 men and women, those who walked at least 6 blocks a day at a normal pace were one-third less likely to have trouble sleeping. Those who picked up the pace fared even better.

YOUR MATTRESS AND PILLOW

In the fairy tale *The Princess and the Pea*, the truth of a maiden's claim of being of royal blood is tested by placing a pea under 20 mattresses and 20 feather beds, because the sleep of only a real princess would be disturbed by something so small. Okay, that's overstating the importance of comfort to sleep. Still, your mattress (and pillow) can mean the difference between a good night's sleep and a nightly marathon of tossing and turning. Here are some tips for outfitting your bed for sound snoozing.

Spring for a new mattress. If you wake up achy each morning, or if your mattress is saggy, lumpy, or more than 7 years old, it's time to invest in a new one.

Firm up a squishy bed. For a temporary fix while you're sizing up a replacement mattress, slide a sheet of ¾-inch plywood between your current mattress and box spring.

Test-drive several models. At the store, lie in your preferred sleep position on each mattress for about 10 minutes. You should feel comfortable and supported, and your back muscles should be relaxed.

Buy for durability. Choose a coil count of at least 400 for a queen mattress and 480 for a king. Make sure that the retailer has an exchange policy; you won't know for several nights whether you've found the right mattress.

Add a pillow to beat back and neck pain. Do you sleep on your back? Tuck an extra pillow under your knees and a smaller one under your lower back. Side sleepers should wedge a flat pillow between their knees; stomach snoozers will want one under their hips.

Get a specialty pillow. A cervical pillow or one made of memory foam is specially contoured to support the neck. Throwing an arm and a leg over a body pillow also can help keep the spine in line. Some medical-supply stores and department stores carry these pillows, as do some specialty linen stores.

Allergy-proof your pillow. Synthetic pillows can hold up to five times as much dust-mite matter as feather pillows, which are encased to prevent feathers from floating away. If you use a synthetic pillow, put it in a plastic cover (underneath your pillowcase) to keep dust mites from aggravating allergy or asthma symptoms.

4 More Sleep-Stealers—Solved!

If your bedroom makeover doesn't produce the desired results, you may need to engage in further sleuthing to figure out just what's hampering your sleep. Experts have identified four situations that can easily keep you from sleeping as well as you should. Do any of these sound familiar?

Your bed is also an entertainment center or workstation. When you habitually work on spreadsheets or watch the 11 o'clock news while propped up on your pillows, your brain learns to associate bed with activity rather than with sleep. It's okay to tune in to TV to relax and unwind, but opt for soothing shows, such as those about nature or animals—and keep your set somewhere other than your bedroom. And definitely shut down your laptop before climbing into bed.

You yak on your cell phone before bed. Turn off your cell and use a landline for nighttime calls. Researchers from Wayne State University, in collaboration with a research team from Sweden, theorize that low-level radiation from cell phones may disrupt production of sleep-inducing melatonin or excite other areas of the brain.

Your pet keeps you awake. While sharing your bed with Fido or Fluffy warms the soul, his or her movements and noises can leave you sleepless. Consider relocating your pooch or kitty to a special sleeping place beside your bed. Don't feel guilty: Once you're well rested, you'll have more energy to give to your pet.

Your partner bugs you in bed. He snores. She tosses, turns, and kicks through the night. If your partner is keeping you awake, you are not alone. According to a 2005 survey administered by the National Sleep Foundation, 38 percent of respondents reported relationship problems related to a partner's sleep disorder.

Snoring is the biggest challenge. You may have tried earplugs; he may have tried nasal strips. The best fix: an honest discussion of the issue and an expression of your concern for his health. Loud snoring—especially if accompanied by choking and gasping—could be a sign of obstructive sleep apnea.

If you choose to sleep in another room as a more or less permanent solution, reassure your partner that going solo won't deep-six your sex life. Agree to regular "date nights" in a bed you share.

TRANSFORMATION TOOL #3: STRESS LESS

Getting a handle on stress is vital to controlling your blood sugar. As a bonus, it can help melt away belly fat, which tends to accumulate in the presence of stress hormones.

You need the skills and tools not only to cope with the stressors that are in your life right now, but also to cultivate the sort of resilient mindset that can keep any stressful situation from getting the best of you. With our C-A-L-M Technique and our Tranquillity Tips, which you'll learn here, you'll be able to shrug off stress—and tighten your control of your blood sugar *and* your weight.

Stress Check #1: C-A-L-M in 4 Easy Steps

We've devised a simple mental exercise, called C-A-L-M, that you can use whenever you find yourself in a stressful situation. It's intended to help you clear your head and short-circuit the fight-or-flight response. Try it the next time you feel your stress level rising; we promise you'll defrazzle in 5 minutes or less.

Center. Find a quiet, comfortable place without distractions. (If you're at work, close your door or borrow an empty office.) Sit with your back straight; rest your hands in a comfortable position. If you like, ask your higher power, such as God, to help you find your center. Let your eyes rest comfortably downward; gaze softly, but do not focus on anything. Let your breathing become deep and rhythmic. It's okay to let your attention drift a bit, but stay relaxed. If your eyelids get heavy, let them close. Don't worry about doing it right. Just be.

Accept. When you feel centered, open your eyes and formally accept your stressor, whatever it is. Say, silently or out loud, "At this moment, my [job, boss, mother, life] is causing me stress. At this moment, I choose to accept it." Repeat it as many times as you wish as you open yourself to your stress. Don't fight it. Sit with it. Give yourself permission to relinquish the illusion of control.

Of course, there's a difference between accepting what (or whom) you can't change and being reluctant to change what you can. To help sort that out, consider the stressor. Then ask yourself, "Are the circumstances beyond my control? Have I done all that I can?" If the answer is yes, move to the next step.

Let go. Formally give up control over the person or event that's stressing you. You might literally give yourself a little shake or brush your shoulders as a sign that you've decided to release your worry or frustration.

Often, letting go is accompanied by a sense of relief and release—sometimes subtle, sometimes quite powerful. You might feel your jaw unclench, your shoulders relax, your mind clear, your heart soften. You might even shed a few tears. That's all good.

What if you can't let go? That's okay, too; just keep trying. Letting go is a skill that takes a lifetime of practice to learn, so we're all perpetual students. But it does get easier with time.

Move on. Get on with your day. With your *life*. This minivisualization can help: Imagine an old-fashioned English garden with a cobblestone path winding its way through the lush and fragrant space. Then see your stressors—your boss, your broken dishwasher, even your diabetes—as cobblestones in that path. Those rough stones lead through some breathtaking scenery, don't they? That's the lesson here: Life is what you make it. So is stress.

Stress Check #2: Bank Tranquillity Points

The C-A-L-M Technique is perfect for dealing with the sorts of stressors that seem to loom large over your home or work life. But what about the more everyday variety of stress—the broken appliances, the unexpected bills, the lost dry cleaning? Sure, they're minor events in the grand scheme of things. But by repeatedly triggering the fight-or-flight response, they, too, can take a toll on your blood sugar and your waistline.

We have the solution—or, rather, 50 solutions! They're called Tranquillity Points—50 simple, fast-working strategies that not only provide instant relaxation but also help build your "immunity" to stress, so you're ready whenever life decides to take a swing at you. We're talking things like making a paper airplane, waving to the stranger in the next car, and chomping bubble gum. (When was the last time you blew a bubble?)

Your mission is to accumulate as many Tranquility Points as you can throughout the day. No need to aim for a specific number; after all, you're under enough pressure already! Just enjoy doing as many as you can. You may be surprised by how easily you can squeeze pleasure and relaxation into your daily routine.

1. Belt out a show tune in the shower.
2. Tickle a baby.
3. Buy a bottle of soap bubbles, the kind you used to blow with a wand as a kid, and keep it in your car. Blow when you're stuck in traffic.
4. Snuggle up with your dog or cat.
5. Go to a local pet store and coo at the puppies and kitties in the window.
6. Make faces in the mirror in the restroom at work. (Best to do this when alone.)
7. On your daily walk, break into a skip for a spell.
8. Teach a kid to fly a kite or operate a remote-control car.
9. Buy yourself a fake-glasses-and-nose set. Wear it around the house when life just feels too hard. Get a few pairs for your family, too.
10. Sing in the rain.
11. Buy a box of Mr. Bubble bubble bath and invite your partner to a tub party.
12. Knit baby hats and booties for a local charity.
13. Ask a friend for a hug.
14. Spread a blanket on your lawn and look at the clouds. Or the stars.
15. Buy a cheap extra umbrella. On the next rainy day, offer it to a stranger.
16. Learn to whistle.
17. Try your luck at yodeling.
18. Reread one of the books you loved as a child.
19. Buy yourself a bouquet of daisies.

20. Plant a seed—any seed—and watch it sprout.

21. Feed the birds.

22. Buy special pens and doodle.

23. Memorize a joke.

24. Buy a Mad Libs book and ask your child or partner to play.

25. Make and throw a paper airplane.

26. Buy a few pieces of bubble gum. Sharpen your bubble-blowing skills.

27. Clean out a closet.

28. Play peekaboo with the baby in the cart in front of you while waiting in the supermarket checkout line.

29. Plan and go on an old-fashioned, honest-to-goodness picnic with someone special.

30. Take a different route to work.

31. Sneak out of work early and go to a matinee.

32. Hang a pretty air freshener in your car.

33. Send a card to someone you haven't seen in years.

34. Go to a kids' peewee baseball game and cheer for everyone.

35. Dine by candlelight.

36. Compliment a surly co-worker.

37. Drag out your high school yearbook and laugh at your senior picture.

38. Buy a coloring book and crayons.

39. During your next argument with your spouse, let him or her win. Giggle to yourself.

40. Ambush your spouse with a Nerf gun.

41. Challenge your kid or grandkid to a lightning round of whatever—checkers, Battleship, Uno.

42. Learn one magic trick from start to finish.

43. If the above tip stresses you out, try a card trick.

44. Buy a collection of cheap 100- or 200-piece jigsaw puzzles. When you're feeling panicked, assemble one. Voilà—instant gratification.

45. Challenge yourself to a game of jacks.

46. Buy a Barrel of Monkeys. Creating a colorful chain of chimps can calm you right down.

47. Tired of high-maintenance manicures? Buff your nails to a high shine.

48. Browse local used-book stores, some of the most relaxing places on the planet.

49. Ditto for tiny, local antiques stores or junk shops.

50. Buy a special candle. Light it and thank your higher power, or the universe, for three things in your life.

By the way, you're welcome to add to this list! Think of the things that make your toes curl or that simply take you outside of the same-old, same-old. Often the most profound sources of pleasure and relaxation are those that grow out of living in the moment, as kids do. These are the Hershey's Kisses of life: You need just one or two a day to feel completely satisfied.

THE 4-WEEK TOTAL TRANSFORMATION

So you've got the first 2 weeks of DTOUR behind you. Way to go! If you're like our DTOUR test panelists, your pants are fitting a little looser, your tummy is looking a little flatter, and you're feeling a little more energized and focused. These are fabulous changes; they show that you're not only losing weight, you're stabilizing your blood sugar, too. With every pound gone, with every blood sugar point down, you're one step closer to staying diabetes free or—if you already have diabetes—to avoiding medications and complications.

Your success so far is just a hint of what's to come over the next 4 weeks. For this phase of DTOUR, which we call the Total Transformation, we're going to mix things up a bit with fresh menu choices plus "helper" lifestyle strategies to add on as you wish. The Total Transformation is meant to be a little more flexible and customizable than the 2-Week Fast Start to help you continue to learn the new habits that will keep you fit and healthy for life.

Let's start with the food—because DTOUR is all about food! For the Total Transformation, you'll be building your own daily menus from a selection of breakfasts, lunches, dinners, and snacks. As you'll see, each menu option comes in a 1,400-calorie version and a 1,600-calorie version. You'll choose the one that matches your daily calorie target. We've done all of the nutritional calculations for you, so no matter how you mix and match, you'll be within range for all of your key nutrients, including the Fat-Fighting 4. How easy is that?

The Total Transformation has a few other bells and whistles that can boost your results over the next 4 weeks. One is the DTOUR Workout, which we introduced starting on page 60. Six days a week, you'll be doing either one of the Cardio Walks (the Fat-Torch or the Calorie-Scorch) or the strength-training routines (the Metabo Moves and the Belly Blast). The workouts are designed to grow with you, increasing in duration and intensity as you become slimmer and fitter.

Throughout Total Transformation, we give you tips and techniques for reducing stress and improving sleep—both of which enhance weight loss and blood sugar control. As in the 2-Week Fast Start, there's space to record your daily blood sugar readings as well as your weekly weigh-ins and monthly waist measurements. You can use the journal block (called "How Did You Do?") to write down anything noteworthy about a particular day, whether it's a recipe you liked, a workout that you breezed through, or a challenging situation that you handled with ease.

You can use these extra tools to customize the Total Transformation to your unique needs and lifestyle. If you'd rather stick with just the diet, as in the 2-Week Fast Start, that's okay, too. Do what feels right for you; you can always add other activities as you go along. Remember, this phase of DTOUR is about more than losing weight and reining in your blood sugar—though you'll definitely be doing both of those things! It's about laying the foundation for a lifestyle that's going to put you in control of your health and whether or not diabetes has a place in it.

Your Awesome 4somes

Building your daily menus is super-easy. Just read through the following lists and choose one breakfast, one lunch, one dinner, and two snacks. One important note: If you've been advised to watch your salt intake, be sure to stick with the lower-sodium meal and snack choices. In general, we recommend limiting sodium consumption to no more than 2,300 milligrams per day.

BREAKFASTS

Breakfast 1

☐ Good Lox Bagel: Spread ½ whole grain bagel (2 ounces) with mixture of 2 tablespoons low-fat cream cheese and 2 ounces canned drained salmon

☐ ½ cup fat-free milk or low-fat, calcium-enriched soy or rice beverage

351 calories, 32 g protein, 33 g carbohydrates, 10 g fat (4 g saturated fat), 61 mg cholesterol, 538 mg sodium

1,600-calorie plan: Use 3 ounces salmon and drink 1 cup fat-free milk or low-fat, calcium-enriched soy or rice beverage.

397 calories, 39 g protein, 33 g carbohydrates, 12 g fat (4 g saturated fat), 80 mg cholesterol, 648 mg sodium

Breakfast 2

☐ Get Up and Go Veggie Omelet: In a pan, heat 2 teaspoons canola, peanut, or olive oil. Add ¼ cup egg substitute (or 1 egg white); ½ cup chopped spinach; ½ cup chopped mushrooms, chopped onion, and finely chopped garlic; and chopped herbs as desired. Cook until set. Top with ¼ cup shredded reduced-fat cheese.

☐ 1 slice reduced-calorie whole grain toast spread with 1 tablespoon fat-free or 1% cottage cheese

☐ 1 cup fat-free milk or low-fat, calcium-enriched soy or rice beverage

347 calories, 25 g protein, 30 g carbohydrates, 16 g fat (5 g saturated fat), 26 mg cholesterol, 552 mg sodium

1,600-calorie plan: Use ½ cup egg substitute (or 2 egg whites), add 1 additional slice (2 slices total) reduced-calorie whole grain toast, and use 2 tablespoons fat-free or 1% cottage cheese.

427 calories, 33 g protein, 43 g carbohydrates, 17 g fat (5 g saturated fat), 27 mg cholesterol, 803 mg sodium

Breakfast 3

☐ Top ½ cup cooked oatmeal with ¼ cup chopped pecans. Sprinkle with ground cinnamon and/or sugar substitute to taste.

☐ ½ cup fat-free or low-fat milk or low-fat, calcium-enriched soy or rice beverage

357 calories, 14 g protein, 30 g carbohydrates, 22 g fat (2 g saturated fat), 5 mg cholesterol, 112 mg sodium

1,600-calorie plan: Eat 1 cup oatmeal and 3 tablespoons chopped pecans (about 15) and drink 1 cup fat-free or low-fat milk or low-fat, calcium-enriched soy or rice beverage.

393 calories, 16 g protein, 43 g carbohydrates, 19 g fat (2 g saturated fat), 5 mg cholesterol, 117 mg sodium

Breakfast 4

☐ On-the-Run Peanut Butter-Banana Toast: Spread 1 slice reduced-calorie whole grain toast with ½ tablespoon all-natural peanut butter and ½ medium sliced banana.

☐ Starbuck's Tall Skinny Latte (made with fat-free or low-fat milk or low-fat, calcium-enriched soy or rice beverage and sugar-free syrup) or 1 cup coffee and 1 cup fat-free milk or low-fat, calcium-enriched soy or rice beverage

351 calories, 18 g protein, 42 g carbohydrates, 13 g fat (2 g saturated fat), 5 mg cholesterol, 289 mg sodium

1,600-calorie plan: Use 2 tablespoons all-natural peanut butter.

404 calories, 20 g protein, 44 g carbohydrates, 17 g fat (3 g saturated fat), 5 mg cholesterol, 301 mg sodium

Breakfast 5

☐ 1 ounce whole grain, flaxseed-enriched cereal (Note: 1 ounce equals the serving size on the Nutrition Facts label.)

☐ 1 cup fat-free milk or low-fat, calcium-enriched soy or rice beverage

☐ 2 tablespoons walnut pieces (about 7 halves)

321 calories, 17 g protein, 41 g carbohydrates, 12 g fat (1 g saturated fat), 5 mg cholesterol, 108 mg sodium

1,600-calorie plan: Use 1 ounce walnut halves (about 14).

411 calories, 19 g protein, 43 g carbohydrates, 21 g fat (2 g saturated fat), 5 mg cholesterol, 108 mg sodium

Breakfast 6

☐ Breakfast Smoothie: In a blender, combine 1 cup fat-free milk or low-fat, calcium-enriched soy or rice beverage; $^3/_4$ cup (6 ounces) fat-free plain yogurt; $^1/_2$ cup sliced strawberries, banana, or other fresh fruit; 2 tablespoons walnuts; and 2 tablespoons flaxseed meal. Add ground cinnamon and/or sugar substitute to taste. Blend for 15 seconds.

344 calories, 22 g protein, 37 g carbohydrates, 14 g fat (1 g saturated fat), 5 mg cholesterol, 224 mg sodium

1,600-calorie plan: Use 1 cup (8 ounces) fat-free plain yogurt.

371 calories, 25 g protein, 42 g carbohydrates, 14 g fat (1 g saturated fat), 5 mg cholesterol, 262 mg sodium

Breakfast 7

❐ Fancy French Toast: Dip 2 slices reduced-calorie whole grain bread into mixture of 1 beaten egg (or $^1/_4$ cup egg substitute); $^1/_4$ cup fat-free milk or low-fat, calcium-enriched soy or rice beverage; and $^1/_2$ teaspoon cinnamon. Melt 1 teaspoon canola oil and 1 teaspoon trans-free canola margarine in hot pan; add bread and grill on both sides until golden brown. Top with 2 tablespoons sugar-free syrup or 1 tablespoon low-calorie syrup. Serve with 1 slice (1 ounce) Canadian-style bacon.

❐ $^1/_2$ cup fat-free milk or low-fat, calcium-enriched soy or rice beverage.

368 calories, 22 g protein, 37 g carbohydrates, 16 g fat (3 g saturated fat), 204 mg cholesterol, 777 mg sodium

1,600-calorie plan: Use 1 whole egg + 1 egg white or $^1/_2$ cup egg substitute.

420 calories, 29 g protein, 42 g carbohydrates, 17 g fat (4 g saturated fat), 390 mg cholesterol, 830 mg sodium

Breakfast 8

❐ Breakfast in a Hurry: 1 can (8 ounces) low-sugar meal-replacement drink, such as Glucerna, Boost Glucose Control, or No Sugar Added Carnation Instant Breakfast

❐ 1 medium orange

❐ 1 tablespoon walnuts or other nuts

364 calories, 12 g protein, 46 g carbohydrates, 15 g fat (1.5 g saturated fat), 2.5 mg cholesterol, 217 mg sodium

1,600-calorie plan: Use 2 tablespoons walnuts or other nuts.

380 calories, 13 g protein, 47 g carbohydrates, 18 g fat (2 g saturated fat), 2.5 mg cholesterol, 217 mg sodium

Breakfast 9

❐ Super White Eggs: Heat 2 teaspoons canola oil in a small skillet. Add 1 whole egg, then 1 egg white around the outside of the whole egg. Cook over low heat until set. Top with 2 tablespoons chopped tomato or salsa. Serve with 1 slice reduced-calorie, high-fiber whole grain toast spread with 1 teaspoon trans-free canola margarine.

❐ 1 cup fat-free milk or low-fat, calcium-enriched soy or rice beverage

351 calories, 21 g protein, 28 g carbohydrates, 19 g fat (3 g saturated fat), 216 mg cholesterol, 620 mg sodium

1,600-calorie plan: Use 1 whole egg, $^1/_2$ teaspoon canola oil, 2 egg whites, and $^1/_2$ teaspoon trans-free canola margarine, and eat 2 slices reduced-calorie, high-fiber whole grain toast spread with 1 teaspoon trans-free canola margarine. Serve with $^3/_4$ cup fat-free milk or low-fat, calcium-enriched soy or rice beverage.

383 calories, 27 g protein, 40 g carbohydrates, 15 g fat (2.5 g saturated fat), 216 mg cholesterol, 817 mg sodium

Breakfast 10

❐ Spread 3 buckwheat or whole wheat pancakes (6" diameter) with 1 teaspoon trans-free canola margarine and $^1/_4$ cup unsweetened applesauce or 2 tablespoons sugar-free syrup, if desired.

❐ 3 ounces Canadian-style bacon

❐ 8 ounces fat-free milk or low-fat, calcium-enriched soy or rice beverage

340 calories, 18 g protein, 36 g carbohydrates, 14 g fat (3 g saturated fat), 54 mg cholesterol, 738 mg sodium

1,600-calorie plan: Eat 4 buckwheat or whole wheat pancakes (6" diameter) spread with 2 teaspoons trans-free canola margarine and $^1/_4$ cup unsweetened applesauce or 2 tablespoons sugar-free syrup, if desired, and add 2 ounces Canadian-style bacon.

398 calories, 24 g protein, 41 g carbohydrates, 16 g fat (3.5 g saturated fat), 80 mg cholesterol, 1173 mg sodium

Breakfast 11

❐ Egg Muffin Olé: Toast 1 whole grain English muffin and top with 1 slice (1 ounce) reduced-fat cheese and 1 egg or $\frac{1}{4}$ cup egg substitute scrambled in 1 teaspoon canola or olive oil. Flavor with $\frac{1}{4}$ cup chopped tomato, onion, and/or salsa.

❐ $\frac{1}{2}$ cup fat-free milk or low-fat, calcium-enriched soy or rice beverage

335 calories, 25 g protein, 39 g carbohydrates, 11 g fat (4 g saturated fat), 17 mg cholesterol, 1039 mg sodium

1,600-calorie plan: Use $\frac{1}{2}$ cup egg substitute, and drink 1 cup fat-free milk or low-fat, calcium-enriched soy or rice beverage.

407 calories, 35 g protein, 46 g carbohydrates, 11 g fat (3.5 g saturated fat), 20 mg cholesterol, 1206 mg sodium

Breakfast 12

❐ Good-Morning Blend: Stir 2 tablespoons dried fruit; 2 tablespoons flaxseed meal; and 2 tablespoons chopped unsalted raw almonds, walnuts, or pecans into 1 cup fat-free or low-fat plain yogurt (no sugar added). Add ground cinnamon and/or sugar substitute to taste.

345 calories, 20 g protein, 38 g carbohydrates, 14 g fat (1 g saturated fat), 5 mg cholesterol, 214 mg sodium

1,600-calorie plan: Use 4 tablespoons chopped nuts.

403 calories, 16 g protein, 34 g carbohydrates, 26 g fat (3 g saturated fat), 10 mg cholesterol, 140 mg sodium

Breakfast 13

❐ Spread $\frac{1}{4}$ cup fat-free or 1% cottage cheese on 2 slices toasted reduced-calorie, high-fiber bread. Top with 2 tablespoons chopped dates or other dried fruit and $\frac{1}{2}$ ounce (about 2 tablespoons) chopped unsalted raw walnuts.

342 calories, 23 g protein, 45 g carbohydrates, 11 g fat (1.5 g saturated fat), 4.5 mg cholesterol, 752 mg sodium

1,600-calorie plan: Use chopped walnuts or other nuts.

400 calories, 25 g protein, 46 g carbohydrates, 16 g fat (1.5 g saturated fat), 4.5 mg cholesterol, 753 mg sodium

Breakfast 14

❐ Breakfast Burrito: Cook $\frac{1}{2}$ cup chopped onions; 1 clove garlic, finely chopped; and $\frac{1}{2}$ cup chopped green, yellow, or red bell pepper in 1 teaspoon olive or canola oil. Add $\frac{1}{4}$ cup egg substitute (or 1 egg white) and cook until set. Place mixture in 1 whole grain tortilla (8"-10" diameter). Sprinkle with 2 tablespoons shredded reduced-fat cheese, 2 tablespoons salsa, and 1 tablespoon reduced-fat sour cream.

364 calories, 20 g protein, 20 g carbohydrates, 14.5 g fat (3.5 g saturated fat), 12 mg cholesterol, 900 mg sodium

1,600-calorie plan: Use 1 cup chopped green, yellow, or red bell pepper, 1 tablespoon olive or canola oil, and 2 tablespoons reduced-fat sour cream.

409 calories, 22 g protein, 47 g carbohydrates, 16 g fat (4.5 g saturated fat), 16 mg cholesterol, 1034 mg sodium

LUNCHES

Lunch 1

❐ Grilled Ham-and-Cheese Reuben: Spread 2 slices reduced-calorie whole grain bread with 1 tablespoon Dijon mustard. Pile 1 ounce (1 slice) reduced-fat Swiss cheese, 1 ounce lean ham, and $\frac{1}{2}$ cup shredded cabbage on top. Spread $\frac{1}{2}$ teaspoon trans-free canola margarine on each outer side. Brown each side in hot pan until cheese melts.

❐ 1 cup (8 ounces) fat-free milk or low-fat, calcium-enriched soy or rice beverage

380 calories, 28 g protein, 41 g carbohydrates, 13 g fat (3.5 g saturated fat), 37 mg cholesterol, 1373 mg sodium

1,600-calorie plan: Use 3 ounces lean ham.

414 calories, 32 g protein, 41 g carbohydrates, 15 g fat (4.5 g saturated fat), 48 mg cholesterol, 1641 mg sodium

Lunch 2

❐ Tuna Pita Pocket: Place sliced tomatoes inside pocket of $\frac{1}{2}$ whole grain pita. Combine 2 ounces water-packed tuna, drained, with 1 tablespoon reduced-

fat mayonnaise (or
1 teaspoon regular mayon-
naise); 1 tablespoon fat-free
plain yogurt; 1 tablespoon
chopped celery; 8 black
olives, chopped; and
1 tablespoon chopped onion.
Season with salt-free herbs
and spices as desired. Add
mixture to pita. Top with
$1/2$ cup fat-free plain yogurt.

324 calories, 26 g protein, 38 g
carbohydrates, 9 g fat (1.5 g saturated
fat), 19 mg cholesterol, 829 mg sodium

1,600-calorie plan: Use
3 ounces water-packed tuna,
drained; and 2 tablespoons
reduced-fat mayonnaise (or
2 teaspoons regular
mayonnaise).

400 calories, 32 g protein, 37 g
carbohydrates, 15 g fat (1.5 g saturated
fat), 30 mg cholesterol, 1120 mg sodium

Lunch 3

❏ D'lightful Sub Salad: Add
2 ounces deli ham and turkey
to 3 cups fresh spinach and
other salad greens. Add 1
tomato, chopped; sliced red
onion; and $1/4$ avocado, sliced.
Top with 2 tablespoons low-
calorie salad dressing and
$1/4$ cup shredded reduced-fat
cheese.

❏ 2 rye crisp crackers

346 calories, 22 g protein, 31 g
carbohydrates, 17 g fat (3.5 g saturated
fat), 34 mg cholesterol, 1148 mg sodium

1,600-calorie plan: Use
3 ounces deli ham and
turkey.

400 calories, 28 g protein, 32 g
carbohydrates, 20 g fat (5 g saturated
fat), 61 mg cholesterol, 1647 mg sodium

Lunch 4

❏ On-the-Go Vegetable
Wrap: Spread 1 whole grain
or high-fiber (at least
5 grams dietary fiber per
serving) vegetable-based
tortilla wrap (8"–10"
diameter) with $1/3$ cup
hummus. Add 2 ounces
turkey breast, $1/2$ cup
shredded cabbage and/or
spinach leaves, and $1/4$ cup
shredded or finely chopped
carrots. Sprinkle with 1 tablespoon seasoned rice vinegar
and roll up tightly.

367 calories, 22 g protein, 45 g
carbohydrates, 15 g fat (1.5 g saturated
fat), 24 mg cholesterol, 1480 mg sodium

1,600-calorie plan: Use
8 green olives, chopped, and
3 ounces turkey breast.

396 calories, 27 g protein, 46 g
carbohydrates, 16 g fat (2 g saturated
fat), 36 mg cholesterol, 1867 mg sodium

Lunch 5

❏ High-fiber antioxidant mix:
Mix 1 cup cooked or canned
red, white, pinto, or black
beans; $1/4$ cup chopped
scallions; and 2 tablespoons
light Italian dressing. Serve
over 2 cups mixed salad
greens. Sprinkle with $1/4$ cup
shredded reduced-fat
cheese.

363 calories, 20 g protein, 49 g
carbohydrates, 9 g fat (3 g saturated
fat), 15 mg cholesterol, 736 mg sodium

1,600-calorie plan: Add
2 tablespoons chopped
unsalted raw nuts.

416 calories, 22 g protein, 50 g
carbohydrates, 15 g fat (3.5 g saturated
fat), 15 mg cholesterol, 726 mg sodium

Lunch 6

❏ Easy Cheesy Quesadilla:
Layer 2 ounces shredded
chicken and 2 tablespoons
shredded reduced-fat
cheese on 1 corn tortilla
(6" diameter). Place another
tortilla on top and cook in a
small pan over medium heat
until cheese melts and
quesadilla is browned on
both sides. (You can also
microwave on medium for
30 to 45 seconds.) Cut into
4 wedges and garnish with
$1/4$ cup salsa. Serve with
2 cups mixed green salad
topped with 2 tablespoons
mashed avocado mixed with
1 tablespoon reduced-fat
sour cream.

369 calories, 29 g protein, 39 g
carbohydrates, 12 g fat (4 g saturated
fat), 62 mg cholesterol, 591 mg sodium

1,600-calorie plan: Use
3 ounces shredded chicken.

415 calories, 38 g protein, 39 g
carbohydrates, 13 g fat (4 g saturated
fat), 86 mg cholesterol, 612 mg sodium

Lunch 7

❏ Banana Split Salad: Split
1 small banana in half
lengthwise. Top with $1/2$ cup
1% or fat-free cottage
cheese and $1/4$ cup unsalted
raw chopped almonds or
other nuts.

❏ $1/2$ cup fat-free milk or low-
fat, calcium-enriched soy or
rice beverage.

360 calories, 24 g protein, 41 g
carbohydrates, 13 g fat (2 g saturated
fat), 7 mg cholesterol, 512 mg sodium

1,600-calorie plan: Use ¾ cup 1% or fat-free cottage cheese and add 1 whole grain crispbread cracker. Skip the milk or soy or rice beverage.

389 calories, 28 g protein, 44 g carbohydrates, 14 g fat (2 g saturated fat), 7 mg cholesterol, 739 mg sodium

Lunch 8

❏ Chicken Salad: Top 2 cups mixed greens, ½ cup chopped tomato, ½ cup sliced cucumber, and ¼ cup chopped carrot with 2 ounces chicken breast. Drizzle with avocado-yogurt dressing (¼ cup mashed avocado, ⅓ cup fat-free plain yogurt, and vinegar and/or herbs to taste).

❏ 1 whole grain crispbread cracker

355 calories, 27 g protein, 33 g carbohydrates, 14 g fat (3 g saturated fat), 53 mg cholesterol, 221 mg sodium

1,600-calorie plan: Use 3 cups mixed greens, 1 cup chopped tomato, and 3 ounces chicken breast.

408 calories, 36 g protein, 34 g carbohydrates, 15 g fat (3 g saturated fat), 77 mg cholesterol, 247 mg sodium

Lunch 9

❏ Tuna Toss: Mix 3 ounces water-packed tuna, drained, with 2 stalks celery, chopped; 4 green olives, chopped; and 1 tablespoon reduced-fat mayonnaise (or 1 teaspoon regular mayonnaise). Add 1 tablespoon seasoned rice vinegar, if desired. Serve on 2 cups mixed dark greens. Top with 1 tablespoon

chopped unsalted raw almonds or other nuts.

❏ 5 whole grain crackers (about 1 ounce)

❏ 1 cup fat-free milk or low-fat, calcium-enriched soy or rice beverage

329 calories, 36 g protein, 19 g carbohydrates, 12 g fat (2 g saturated fat), 46 mg cholesterol, 719 mg sodium

1,600-calorie plan: Use 2 tablespoons reduced-fat mayonnaise (or 2 teaspoons regular); and 3 cups mixed dark greens.

407 calories, 38 g protein, 21 g carbohydrates, 19 g fat (2.5 g saturated fat), 48 mg cholesterol, 751 mg sodium

Lunch 10

❏ Hearty Burger: 3 ounces cooked lean hamburger (or soy vegetable patty), lettuce, tomato, mustard, and 1 tablespoon ketchup on a whole grain bun

❏ 8 baby carrots dipped in 1 tablespoon reduced-fat ranch dressing.

❏ 12 ounces light lemonade or diet soda (look for a product with less than 5 calories per serving).

372 calories, 29 g protein, 39 g carbohydrates, 12 g fat (3.5 g saturated fat), 67 mg cholesterol, 703 mg sodium

1,600-calorie plan: Use 2 tablespoons reduced-fat ranch dressing.

401 calories, 29 g protein, 38 g carbohydrates, 15 g fat (4 g saturated fat), 69 mg cholesterol, 845 mg sodium

Lunch 11

❏ Bean Tostada: Bake 1 corn tortilla (6" diameter) in a hot

oven (400°F) until dry. Spread with ¼ cup cooked or canned pinto beans (rinsed) and 2 tablespoons shredded reduced-fat Mexican-blend cheese. Return to oven for 5 to 10 minutes or microwave on medium for 30 to 45 seconds until cheese melts. Top with ¼ cup salsa.

❏ Cabbage Salad: Mix 1 cup shredded cabbage with 1 chopped tomato and 2 tablespoons light salad dressing.

288 calories, 9 g protein, 43 g carbohydrates, 11 g fat (3 g saturated fat), 17 mg cholesterol, 1191 mg sodium

1,600-calorie plan: Use ½ cup cooked or canned pinto beans (rinsed). Add 2 ounces cooked lean ground beef.

407 calories, 25 g protein, 47 g carbohydrates, 14 g fat (4.5 g saturated fat), 60 mg cholesterol, 1350 mg sodium

Lunch 12

❏ Easy Mix-Up Salad: Toss 3 cups mixed salad greens, ½ cup 1% cottage cheese, 1 tangerine or small orange divided into sections, and 2 tablespoons light Italian dressing. Top with 1 tablespoon unsalted raw chopped almonds or walnuts.

❏ 5 whole grain crackers (such as Triscuits)

337 calories, 19 g protein, 35 g carbohydrates, 14 g fat (2 g saturated fat), 5 mg cholesterol, 835 mg sodium

1,600-calorie plan: Use 1 cup 1% cottage cheese.

418 calories, 33 g protein, 38 g carbohydrates, 15 g fat (3 g saturated fat), 9 mg cholesterol, 1294 mg sodium

Lunch 13

❏ Taco No Taco: Mix 2 ounces grilled fish, chicken, or lean beef; $1/3$ cup brown rice; and $1/2$ cup cooked red, black, or pinto beans.
Top with 2 tablespoons shredded reduced-fat cheese. Top with $1/4$ cup salsa and 1 tablespoon reduced-fat sour cream. Serve over 2 cups mixed lettuce greens.

370 calories, 30 g protein, 41 g carbohydrates, 9 g fat (3 g saturated fat), 54 mg cholesterol, 548 mg sodium

1,600-calorie plan: Use 3 ounces grilled fish.

422 calories, 38 g protein, 41 g carbohydrates, 12 g fat (3.5 g saturated fat), 74 mg cholesterol, 564 mg sodium

Lunch 14

❏ Pesto Pizza: Split and toast a whole grain English muffin. Spread with 1 tablespoon basil pesto sauce such as Buitoni brand. Top each half with 1 slice tomato (or $1/2$ cup canned tomatoes) and $1/2$ slice reduced-fat cheese. Broil or bake until cheese melts.

❏ $1/2$ cup fat-free milk or low-fat, calcium-enriched soy or rice beverage

354 calories, 20 g protein, 40 g carbohydrates, 14 g fat (6 g saturated fat), 27 mg cholesterol, 840 mg sodium

1,600-calorie plan: Use 2 tablespoons basil pesto sauce.

428 calories, 22 g protein, 42 g carbohydrates, 21 g fat (7 g saturated fat), 32 mg cholesterol, 980 mg sodium

DINNERS

Dinner 1

❏ 3 ounces grilled lean beef top round or sirloin

❏ Cheesy mashed cauliflower: Mash 1 cup cooked cauliflower with $1/4$ cup fat-free milk or low-fat, calcium-enriched soy or rice beverage and 2 tablespoons shredded reduced-fat cheese. Season with Mrs. Dash or other salt-free herbal seasoning

❏ 2 cups mixed green salad with 2 tablespoons light salad dressing

❏ 1 rye crisp cracker

363 calories, 40 g protein, 20 g carbohydrates, 14 g fat (4 g saturated fat), 88 mg cholesterol, 491 mg sodium

1,600-calorie plan: Have 2 rye crisp crackers and add $1/2$ cup fat-free milk or low-fat, calcium-enriched soy or rice beverage.

435 calories, 45 g protein, 33 g carbohydrates, 15 g fat (4 g saturated fat), 90 mg cholesterol, 592 mg sodium

Dinner 2

❏ Grilled Tomato Melt: Place 1 ounce (1 slice) fat-free mozzarella cheese on 1 slice high-fiber, reduced-calorie bread. Add 2 thick slices fresh tomato and several leaves of fresh spinach or basil. Top with another slice bread. Spread $1/2$ teaspoon trans-free canola margarine on outside of each bread slice. Place sandwich in hot skillet over medium heat and cook until both sides are browned and cheese is melted.

❏ 1 cup fat-free milk or low-fat, calcium-enriched soy or rice beverage

322 calories, 21 g protein, 42 g carbohydrates, 10 g fat (4 g saturated fat), 23 mg cholesterol, 622 mg sodium

1,600-calorie plan: Add 1 ounce deli chicken or turkey and 2 tablespoons mashed avocado.

400 calories, 27 g protein, 46 g carbohydrates, 15 g fat (4.5 g saturated fat), 35 mg cholesterol, 908 mg sodium

Dinner 3

❏ 3 ounces grilled salmon

❏ 1 large steamed artichoke or 2 cups broccoli drizzled with mixture of 1 tablespoon reduced-calorie mayonnaise (or 1 teaspoon regular mayonnaise) and 1 tablespoon lemon juice

❏ Garlic Toast: Toast 1 slice sourdough bread and spread with mixture of 1 teaspoon olive oil and 1 clove garlic, finely chopped. Place in hot oven or under broiler until browned.

372 calories, 28 g protein, 31 g carbohydrates, 16 g fat (2.5 g saturated fat), 62 mg cholesterol, 309 mg sodium

1,600-calorie plan: Eat 4 ounces grilled salmon.

423 calories, 36 g protein, 31 g carbohydrates, 18 g fat (3 g saturated fat), 82 mg cholesterol, 325 mg sodium

Dinner 4

❏ 3 ounces grilled chicken breast, seasoned with lemon

pepper or other salt-free seasoning mix

❏ $\frac{1}{2}$ oven-baked potato (about 3 ounces): Slice potato lengthwise, drizzle cut side with 1 teaspoon olive oil, and bake, cut side down, in a 400°F oven for 30 minutes.

❏ Garlic roasted asparagus or green beans: Preheat oven to 400°F. Toss 10 medium (5-7" long) asparagus spears or 2 cups green beans in 1 teaspoon olive oil and finely chopped garlic to taste. Roast for 20 minutes.

358 calories, 35 g protein, 30 g carbohydrates, 12 g fat (2 g saturated fat), 72 mg cholesterol, 78 mg sodium

1,600-calorie plan: Eat 1 whole oven-baked potato (6 ounces).

438 calories, 37 g protein, 48 g carbohydrates, 13 g fat (2 g saturated fat), 72 mg cholesterol, 86 mg sodium

Dinner 5

❏ Tofu Stir-fry: Stir-fry 3 ounces tofu, 1 cup broccoli florets, $\frac{3}{4}$ cup chopped cauliflower, $\frac{1}{2}$ cup sliced carrot, 2 slices scallion, and 2 cloves garlic in 2 table-spoons reduced-sodium stir-fry sauce and 2 teaspoons olive oil. Serve over $\frac{1}{3}$ cup cooked brown rice.

335 calories, 15 g protein, 38 g carbohydrates, 16 g fat (2 g saturated fat), 0 mg cholesterol, 610 mg sodium

1,600-calorie plan: Use 4 ounces tofu and $\frac{1}{2}$ cup cooked brown rice.

392 calories, 18 g protein, 46 g carbohydrates, 18 g fat (2.5 g saturated fat), 0 mg cholesterol, 614 mg sodium

Dinner 6

❏ 3 ounces fish, such as haddock or cod, seasoned with lemon and other salt-free seasonings

❏ Preheat oven to 400°F. Toss $\frac{1}{2}$ cup sliced mushrooms, $\frac{1}{2}$ cup sliced onion, 1 cup chopped zucchini and/ or yellow squash, $\frac{1}{2}$ cup chopped bell pepper, and $\frac{1}{2}$ cup chopped red potato in 2 teaspoons olive oil. Sprinkle with Mrs. Dash or other salt-free herb seasoning. Bake for 30 minutes or until browned and tender.

❏ $\frac{1}{2}$ cup fat-free milk or low-fat, calcium-enriched soy or rice beverage

326 calories, 30 g protein, 30 g carbohydrates, 10 g fat (1.5 g saturated fat), 65 mg cholesterol, 146 mg sodium

1,600-calorie plan: Eat 4 ounces fish and have 1 cup fat-free milk or low-fat, calcium-enriched soy or rice beverage.

399 calories, 41 g protein, 36 g carbohydrates, 11 g fat (1.5 g saturated fat), 89 mg cholesterol, 222 mg sodium

Dinner 7

❏ 3 ounces roast beef or pork tenderloin

❏ 2 cups spinach salad with chopped red bell peppers, 1 tablespoon slivered almonds, and 2 tablespoons light Italian dressing

❏ $\frac{2}{3}$ cup wild rice

336 calories, 23 g protein, 33 g carbohydrates, 13 g fat (1.5 g saturated fat), 40 mg cholesterol, 784 mg sodium

1,600-calorie plan: Eat 4 ounces roast beef or pork tenderloin and 1 cup wild rice.

422 calories, 30 g protein, 45 g carbohydrates, 15 g fat (2 g saturated fat), 54 mg cholesterol, 954 mg sodium

Dinner 8

❏ Grilled Fish Tacos: Tuck 2 ounces grilled fish and 1 cup shredded cabbage sprinkled with seasoned rice vinegar into 1 corn tortilla (6" diameter). Top with 1 tablespoon reduced-fat sour cream.

❏ Grilled or Roasted Vegetables: Marinate 1 cup chopped eggplant, $\frac{1}{2}$ cup chopped mushrooms, $\frac{1}{2}$ cup green beans, and 2 tablespoons chopped onions in 2 tablespoons light Italian dressing and 1 teaspoon olive oil. Grill or roast at 400°F for 30 to 45 minutes or until lightly browned.

367 calories, 23 g protein, 35 g carbohydrates, 16 g fat (2.5 g saturated fat), 45 mg cholesterol, 305 mg sodium

1,600-calorie plan: Eat 3 ounces grilled fish and 2 corn tortillas. For the vegetables, use 1 tablespoon light Italian dressing.

449 calories, 31 g protein, 45 g carbohydrates, 17 g fat (3 g saturated fat), 65 mg cholesterol, 218 mg sodium

Dinner 9

❏ $\frac{1}{2}$ cup cooked whole wheat spaghetti tossed in

finely chopped garlic to taste and 1 teaspoon olive oil

❑ 3 ounces lean meatballs (made with turkey, chicken, or soy)

❑ 1 teaspoon grated Parmesan cheese

❑ Cucumber salad: On bed of 1 cup mixed greens, arrange 1 cup cucumber slices; 10 cherry tomatoes, halved; and ¼ cup chopped red onion. Drizzle with 2 tablespoons light Italian dressing.

351 calories, 15 g protein, 41 g carbohydrates, 16 g fat (3 g saturated fat), 24 mg cholesterol, 580 mg sodium

1,600-calorie plan: Eat 4 ounces lean meatballs (made with turkey, chicken, or soy) and add ½ cup fat-free milk or low-fat, calcium-enriched soy or rice beverage.

423 calories, 21 g protein, 48 g carbohydrates, 18 g fat (3.5 g saturated fat), 34 mg cholesterol, 733 mg sodium

Dinner 10

❑ 1 cup Progresso Healthy Classics or Campbell's Healthy Request canned beef barley or bean soup

❑ Spinach Salad: Toss 2 cups fresh spinach with 1 tablespoon olive oil and balsamic vinegar dressing. Top with 1 tablespoon shredded reduced-fat mozzarella cheese and 1 tablespoon slivered unsalted raw almonds or other nuts.

334 calories, 17 g protein, 22 g carbohydrates, 20 g fat (3.5 g saturated fat), 24 mg cholesterol, 620 mg sodium

1,600-calorie plan: Eat 1½ cups soup.

402 calories, 23 g protein, 31 g carbohydrates, 21 g fat (4 g saturated fat), 34 mg cholesterol, 884 mg sodium

Dinner 11

❑ Grilled Chicken Caesar Salad: 2 cups romaine or other mixed lettuce greens, 2 ounces grilled chicken, and 2 tablespoons reduced-fat Caesar dressing (or 1 tablespoon regular Caesar dressing).

❑ 1 ounce whole grain crackers

❑ 8 ounces fat-free milk or low-fat, calcium-enriched soy or rice beverage

337 calories, 29 g protein, 32 g carbohydrates, 10 g fat (2 g saturated fat), 53 mg cholesterol, 514 mg sodium

1,600-calorie plan: Use 3 cups romaine or other mixed lettuce greens and 3 ounces grilled chicken.

394 calories, 39 g protein, 34 g carbohydrates, 12 g fat (2 g saturated fat), 77 mg cholesterol, 539 mg sodium

Dinner 12

❑ Oven-Fried Chicken: Preheat oven to 350°F. Toss 3 ounces raw chicken breast in 1 tablespoon light Italian dressing. Coat with 2 table-spoons seasoned bread crumbs; spray lightly with canola cooking spray. Place on lightly oiled cookie sheet. Bake for 30 minutes or until browned and no longer pink inside.

❑ Perky Tomato Salad: Toss together 1 cup coarsely

chopped tomatoes, 1 cup torn red or green leaf lettuce, and 1 tablespoon fresh basil (or 1 teaspoon dried basil). Drizzle with a mixture of 1 teaspoon olive oil and 1 teaspoon balsamic vinegar. Top with 1 tablespoon toasted pine nuts.

343 calories, 23 g protein, 19 g carbohydrates, 20 g fat (2.5 g saturated fat), 49 mg cholesterol, 433 mg sodium

1,600-calorie plan: Use 4 ounces raw chicken breast, 4 tablespoons seasoned bread crumbs, and 2 tablespoons toasted pine nuts.

428 calories, 33.5 g protein, 29 g carbohydrates, 20 g fat (2.5 g saturated fat), 73 mg cholesterol, 718 mg sodium

Dinner 13

❑ Lazy Chef Salad: Toss together 2 cups mixed salad greens; 2 ounces water-packed canned tuna or salmon, drained; ¼ cup cooked chickpeas; 2 tablespoons shredded reduced-fat cheese; and 2 tablespoons reduced-fat ranch dressing.

❑ 1 rye crisp cracker

❑ ½ cup fat-free milk or low-fat, calcium-enriched soy or rice beverage

349 calories, 28 g protein, 33 g carbohydrates, 11 g fat (3 g saturated fat), 34 mg cholesterol, 839 mg sodium

1,600-calorie plan: Use 3 cups mixed salad greens and 3 ounces canned water-packed tuna or salmon, drained. Drink 1 cup fat-free milk or low-fat, calcium-enriched soy or rice beverage.

430 calories, 39 g protein, 40 g carbohydrates, 12 g fat (3.5 g saturated fat), 45 mg cholesterol, 991 mg sodium

Dinner 14

❑ Grilled Fajitas: Heat 1 teaspoon olive oil in a skillet. Add 2 ounces chicken breast, pork, or beef tenderloin; ½ cup sliced onion; 1 cup chopped green and red bell peppers; ½ cup sliced carrots; and 2 cloves garlic, and sauté. Serve on 1 corn tortilla.

❑ ½ cup fat-free milk or low-fat, calcium-enriched soy or rice beverage

359 calories, 25 g protein, 40 g carbohydrates, 11 g fat (3 g saturated fat), 55 mg cholesterol, 147 mg sodium

1,600-calorie plan: Use 3 ounces chicken breast, pork, or beef tenderloin.

417 calories, 33 g protein, 40 g carbohydrates, 14 g fat (4 g saturated fat), 80 mg cholesterol, 164 mg sodium

SNACKS

Snack 1

❑ Mix together ⅓ cup fat-free or 1% cottage cheese and ½ cup chopped peaches (fresh or canned in water or juice, drained). Top with 2 tablespoons chopped unsalted raw almonds, walnuts, or other nuts.

177 calories, 12 g protein, 21 g carbohydrates, 6 g fat (0.5 g saturated fat), 3 mg cholesterol, 284 mg sodium

1,600-calorie plan: Use ½ cup fat-free or 1% cottage cheese and 1 cup chopped peaches.

205 calories, 17 g protein, 24 g carbohydrates, 6 g fat (0.5 g saturated fat), 5 mg cholesterol, 430 mg sodium

Snack 2

❑ 3 tablespoons unsalted raw walnuts or other nuts

❑ 1 tablespoon mixed dried fruits (blueberries, cherries, cranberries, and/or raisins)

168 calories, 4 g protein, 10 g carbohydrates, 14 g fat (1.5 g saturated fat), 0 mg cholesterol, 9 mg sodium

1,600-calorie plan: Eat 2 tablespoons dried fruits.

193 calories, 4 g protein, 16 g carbohydrates, 14 g fat (1.5 g saturated fat), 0 mg cholesterol, 18 mg sodium

Snack 3

❑ 1 ounce reduced-fat cheese

❑ 1 medium apple

152 calories, 7 g protein, 20 g carbohydrates, 6 g fat (3.5 g saturated fat), 20 mg cholesterol, 241 mg sodium

1,600-calorie plan: Use 1 tablespoon natural peanut butter and cut the apple into slices (about ½ cup).

177 calories, 4 g protein, 22 g carbohydrates, 8 g fat (1 g saturated fat), 0 mg cholesterol, 61 mg sodium

Snack 4

❑ ⅔ cup fat-free or low-fat yogurt (6 ounces)

❑ ½ cup fresh or frozen blueberries

❑ 1 tablespoon chopped unsalted raw nuts

169 calories, 10 g protein, 26 g carbohydrates, 5 g fat (0.5 g saturated fat), 0 mg cholesterol, 116 mg sodium

1,600-calorie plan: Use 2 tablespoons chopped nuts.

217 calories, 11 g protein, 26 g carbohydrates, 10 g fat (1 g saturated fat), 0 mg cholesterol, 116 mg sodium

Snack 5

❑ 2 fig cookies

❑ 1 cup fat-free milk or low-fat, calcium-enriched soy or rice beverage

193 calories, 9 g protein, 34 g carbohydrates, 3 g fat (0.5 g saturated fat), 5 mg cholesterol, 218 mg sodium

1,600-calorie plan: Same as above.

Snack 6

❑ ½ cup light ice cream

❑ 1 tablespoon reduced-fat chocolate syrup

❑ 1 tablespoon chopped unsalted raw nuts

190 calories, 4 g protein, 25 g carbohydrates, 9 g fat (2.5 g saturated fat), 36 mg cholesterol, 67 mg sodium

1,600-calorie plan: Same as above.

Snack 7

❑ 6 cups reduced-fat popcorn sprinkled with 2 tablespoons grated Parmesan cheese

❑ 12 ounces diet soda or sugar-free beverage

165 calories, 8 g protein, 25 g carbohydrates, 6 g fat (1.5 g saturated fat), 9 mg cholesterol, 435 mg sodium

1,600-calorie plan: Add
1 ounce beef jerky.

165 calories, 8 g protein, 25 g
carbohydrates, 6 g fat (1.5 g saturated
fat), 9 mg cholesterol, 435 mg sodium

Snack 8

❑ 1 ounce mozzarella string
cheese

❑ 2 fresh or dried figs

200 calories, 8 g protein, 28 g
carbohydrates, 6 g fat (4 g saturated
fat), 20 mg cholesterol, 240 mg sodium

1,600-calorie plan: Add
7 walnut halves.

200 calories, 8 g protein, 28 g
carbohydrates, 6 g fat (4 g saturated
fat), 20 mg cholesterol, 240 mg sodium

Snack 9

❑ 4 tablespoons hummus or
1 tablespoon natural peanut
butter

❑ 2 whole grain crispbread

173 calories, 4 g protein, 26 g
carbohydrates, 6 g fat (0 g saturated
fat), 0 mg cholesterol, 373 mg sodium

1,600-calorie plan: Have
3 whole grain cripsbreads.

210 calories, 4 g protein, 35 g
carbohydrates, 6 g fat (0 g saturated
fat), 0 mg cholesterol, 399 mg sodium

Snack 10

❑ 2 tablespoons walnut
halves or other nut halves

❑ 3 fresh apricots or 6 dried
apricot halves

146 calories, 4 g protein, 14 g
carbohydrates, 10 g fat (1 g saturated
fat), 0 mg cholesterol, 1.5 mg sodium

1,600-calorie plan: Have
2 tablespoons walnut halves
or other nut halves and

4 fresh apricots or 8 dried
apricot halves.

163 calories, 4 g protein, 18 g
carbohydrates, 10 g fat (1 g saturated
fat), 0 mg cholesterol, 1.5 mg sodium

Snack 11

❑ Turkey or Chicken
Sandwich: Spread 1 slice
reduced-calorie whole grain
bread with 1 tablespoon
reduced-fat mayonnaise (or
1 teaspoon regular mayon-
naise). Cut bread in half and
pile 2 ounces sliced turkey or
chicken breast and ¼ cup
shredded lettuce on one side.
Top with other half of bread.

❑ ½ cup cherry tomatoes.

164 calories, 13 g protein, 20 g
carbohydrates, 5 g fat (1 g saturated
fat), 28 mg cholesterol, 795 mg sodium

1,600-calorie plan: Use 2
slices reduced-calorie whole
grain bread.

220 calories, 15 g protein, 32 g
carbohydrates, 6 g fat (1 g saturated
fat), 28 mg cholesterol, 938 mg sodium

Snack 12

❑ Bone-Soothing Hot
Chocolate: Mix ⅓ cup fat-
free powdered milk with
1 tablespoon cocoa powder
and 1 teaspoon sugar
substitute. Add 8 ounces
boiling water and stir.
Top with 1 regular-size
marshmallow.

❑ 3 small no-sugar-added
gingersnap cookies (serving
size not to exceed 15 grams
total carbohydrates; Murray
Sugar Free is one brand.)

170 calories, 10 g protein, 31 g
carbohydrates, 3 g fat (1 g saturated
fat), 4 mg cholesterol, 181 mg sodium

1,600-calorie plan: Have
4 small no-sugar-added
gingersnap cookies.

189 calories, 10 g protein, 34 g
carbohydrates, 4 g fat (1 g saturated
fat), 4 mg cholesterol, 199 mg sodium

Snack 13

❑ 3 graham cracker squares
spread with 1 teaspoon all-
natural peanut or other nut
butter

❑ ½ cup fat-free or low-fat
milk or low-fat, calcium-
enriched soy or rice
beverage

174 calories, 7 g protein, 26 g
carbohydrates, 5 g fat (1 g saturated
fat), 2.5 mg cholesterol, 202 mg
sodium

1,600-calorie plan: Use
2 teaspoons all-natural
peanut or other nut butter.

209 calories, 8 g protein, 27 g
carbohydrates, 8 g fat (1 g saturated
fat), 2.5 mg cholesterol, 210 mg sodium

Snack 14

❑ 1 cup raw fresh sugar snap
peas

❑ 2 tablespoons reduced-fat
ranch dressing

❑ 1 ounce string cheese

195 calories, 12 g protein, 16 g
carbohydrates, 10 g fat (4.5 g saturated
fat), 23 mg cholesterol, 527 mg sodium

1,600-calorie plan: Eat
1 ½ cups sugar snap peas.

191 calories, 8 g protein, 25 g
carbohydrates, 7 g fat (1 g saturated
fat), 5 mg cholesterol, 503 mg sodium

DAY
1

Your Awesome 4somes

BREAKFAST

LUNCH

SNACK 1

DINNER

SNACK 2

Your DTOUR Workout

☐ Fat-Torch Walk (page 55), 20 minutes

> All glory comes from daring to begin.
> —WILLIAM SHAKESPEARE

HOW DID YOU DO?

BALANCE YOUR BLOOD SUGAR

	TIME	READING
CHECK 1		
CHECK 2		
CHECK 3		
CHECK 4		
CHECK 5		

MEASURE YOURSELF

Your weight: _____ pounds

Your waistline: _____ inches

SUCCEED ALL DAY

Try iPod therapy. Create an upbeat playlist on your MP3 player to help you deal with cravings. When you're blindsided by a yen for pizza, ice cream, or chocolate, crank up those tunes. The music will distract you and provide the emotional release you'd get from indulging your craving.

Give yourself some props. It's more challenging to start a fitness program—or start one again—than to continue one. It takes more determination, planning, encouragement—and a major shot of courage. On Day 1, give yourself credit for tackling such a demanding task.

Your Awesome 4somes

BREAKFAST

LUNCH

SNACK 1

DINNER

SNACK 2

Your DTOUR Workout

☐ Metabo Moves (page 60)
☐ Belly Blast (page 65)

It's always fun to do the impossible.
—WALT DISNEY

HOW DID YOU DO?

BALANCE YOUR BLOOD SUGAR

	TIME	READING
CHECK 1		
CHECK 2		
CHECK 3		
CHECK 4		
CHECK 5		

SUCCEED ALL DAY

Hang with optimists. Who do you know who's relentlessly cheerful and optimistic? A parent at your child's soccer game? Your sister? Whoever it is, make an effort to spend more time with him or her. Call her to chat. Invite him out for coffee. It's hard to fret when you're bathing in positive vibes.

Sniff the sweet scent of slumber. Sprinkle a few drops of pure lavender essential oil (available at health-food stores) on a tissue and tuck it under your pillow. Research shows that the scent of this pretty purple flower eases insomnia. Plus, the scent of lavender is heavenly.

Your Awesome 4somes

BREAKFAST

LUNCH

SNACK 1

DINNER

SNACK 2

Your DTOUR Workout

☐ Calorie-Scorch Walk (page 55), 15 minutes

> Your future is created by what you
> do today, not tomorrow.
> —ROBERT KIYOSAKI

HOW DID YOU DO?

BALANCE YOUR BLOOD SUGAR

	TIME	READING
CHECK 1		
CHECK 2		
CHECK 3		
CHECK 4		
CHECK 5		

SUCCEED ALL DAY

Walk off winter cravings. Seasonal affective disorder (SAD), a reaction to reduced sunlight during the winter months, creates cravings for highly refined carbohydrates. If you suspect SAD is at the root of your cravings, soak up natural light on daily walks until the longer days of spring arrive.

Learn to say "The world won't end." This phrase is an all-purpose stress reliever, and it will help you put your life in perspective. The car didn't get washed this weekend? The world won't end.

DAY
4

Your Awesome 4somes

BREAKFAST

LUNCH

SNACK 1

DINNER

SNACK 2

Your DTOUR Workout

☐ Rest Day

> If you really want something,
> you can figure out how to make it happen.
> —CHER

HOW DID YOU DO?

BALANCE YOUR BLOOD SUGAR

	TIME	READING
CHECK 1		
CHECK 2		
CHECK 3		
CHECK 4		
CHECK 5		

SUCCEED ALL DAY

Set specific goals. *What exercises will you do, when, and where?* A specific goal might be "I will do three Cardio Walks at 6:45 a.m. before work and two on the weekends and the Belly Blast and Metabo Moves before dinner on Mondays, Wednesdays, and Fridays."

Question your meds. Certain over-the-counter and prescription medications, particularly those that treat colds and allergies, heart disease, high blood pressure, and pain, can keep you awake. If you take prescription medication routinely, ask your doctor about the side effects. If she suspects the drug could be interfering with your sleep, she may be able to substitute another one or change the time of day you take it.

DAY
5

Your Awesome 4somes

BREAKFAST

LUNCH

SNACK 1

DINNER

SNACK 2

Your DTOUR Workout
☐ Fat-Torch Walk (page 55), 20 minutes

> It is hard to fail, but it is worse never
> to have tried to succeed.
> —THEODORE ROOSEVELT

HOW DID YOU DO?

BALANCE YOUR BLOOD SUGAR

	TIME	READING
CHECK 1		
CHECK 2		
CHECK 3		
CHECK 4		
CHECK 5		

SUCCEED ALL DAY

Replace images of food with other pleasant images. Imagining a steaming, gooey slice of pizza? Instead, imagine walking on the beach in a flattering bathing suit. Swapping images may work better than trying to quash a particular craving.

Resist the urge to sleep in. Late night? Get up within an hour of your usual rising time. It's fine to catnap for 30 minutes to make up for lost slumber. Nap longer than that, however, and you may have trouble getting to sleep come bedtime.

Your Awesome 4somes

BREAKFAST

LUNCH

SNACK 1

DINNER

SNACK 2

Your DTOUR Workout

☐ Metabo Moves (page 60)
☐ Belly Blast (page 65)

> People often say that motivation
> doesn't last. Well, neither does bathing—
> that's why we recommend it daily.
> —ZIG ZIGLAR

HOW DID YOU DO?

BALANCE YOUR BLOOD SUGAR

	TIME	READING
CHECK 1		
CHECK 2		
CHECK 3		
CHECK 4		
CHECK 5		

SUCCEED ALL DAY

Set action-oriented goals.
Here's a take-action goal tailor-made for you: Resolve to walk for at least 30 minutes four times a week. Another: Aim to shake 5 minutes off your Calorie-Scorch Walk by the end of the program.

Make time for a morning hug.
Before you head out the door, take 10 seconds to hold your partner in your arms. That simple embrace can help you stay calmer throughout the entire day, researchers at the University of North Carolina at Chapel Hill found.

Your Awesome 4somes

BREAKFAST

LUNCH

SNACK 1

DINNER

SNACK 2

Your DTOUR Workout

☐ Calorie-Scorch Walk (page 55), 15 minutes

> What would you attempt to do
> if you knew you would not fail?
> —ROBERT SCHULLER

HOW DID YOU DO?

BALANCE YOUR BLOOD SUGAR

	TIME	READING
CHECK 1		
CHECK 2		
CHECK 3		
CHECK 4		
CHECK 5		

MEASURE YOURSELF

Your weight: _____ pounds

SUCCEED ALL DAY

Silence your sweet tooth. To block a craving for sweets, rinse your mouth with 30 drops of a tincture of the Indian herb gymnema mixed with water, suggests Andrew Weil, MD. You'll find gymnema in health-food stores.

Set realistic goals. They should be challenging, but doable. If a goal is too hard (like wanting to run 10 miles when you have yet to run 1), you'll get discouraged. If it's too easy, you won't feel much satisfaction when you achieve it.

DAY
8

Your Awesome 4somes

BREAKFAST

LUNCH

SNACK 1

DINNER

SNACK 2

Your DTOUR Workout

☐ Fat-Torch Walk (page 55), 25 minutes

> # Smooth seas do not make skillful sailors.
> ## —AFRICAN PROVERB

HOW DID YOU DO?

BALANCE YOUR BLOOD SUGAR

	TIME	READING
CHECK 1		
CHECK 2		
CHECK 3		
CHECK 4		
CHECK 5		

SUCCEED ALL DAY

Tame stress together. Chances are that life is stressful for your partner, too. Start a discussion aimed at helping you both recognize and, more important, defuse each other's stressors. How about a shared glass of wine, or a mutual foot rub?

Play sleuth to your sleeplessness. Keep a sleep log for a week. Record what times you go to bed and wake up, the total number of hours of sleep you get, whether you awaken during the night and what you do (toss and turn, read, watch TV), how much and at what time you ingest caffeine and/or alcohol, your emotional state (anxious, excited), and at what time you took any over-the-counter or prescription medications.

Your Awesome 4somes

BREAKFAST

LUNCH

SNACK 1

DINNER

SNACK 2

Your DTOUR Workout:

☐ Metabo Moves (page 60)
☐ Belly Blast (page 65)

> If you can't make a mistake,
> you can't make anything.
> —MARVA COLLINS

HOW DID YOU DO?

BALANCE YOUR BLOOD SUGAR

	TIME	READING
CHECK 1		
CHECK 2		
CHECK 3		
CHECK 4		
CHECK 5		

SUCCEED ALL DAY

Refuel every 4 hours. Regular eating keeps blood sugar stable, which prevents you from feeling famished. If you're hungry between meals, a 150-calorie snack such as string cheese, fruit, and unsalted raw nuts should hold you over.

Turn unknowns into knowns. If your stress is caused by unknown dangers, choose education over anxiety. Make reasonable plans to take precautions, then live your life. Turn off the television and radio if the news increases your anxiety. Plan activities that are familiar and rewarding–doing yard work, cleaning out the attic or garage, taking a long walk or hike.

Your Awesome 4somes

BREAKFAST

LUNCH

SNACK 1

DINNER

SNACK 2

Your DTOUR Workout

☐ Calorie-Scorch Walk (page 55), 20 minutes

> That some achieve great success, is proof
> to all that others can achieve it as well.
> —ABRAHAM LINCOLN

HOW DID YOU DO?

BALANCE YOUR BLOOD SUGAR

	TIME	READING
CHECK 1		
CHECK 2		
CHECK 3		
CHECK 4		
CHECK 5		

SUCCEED ALL DAY

Be alert to prime dropout time. About half of new exercisers quit within a few months, research shows. But support can keep your momentum going. If you struggle with exercise, begin a walking or fitness group. If you're goal focused, sign up for an event that's a few months away, like a 5- or 10-K walk.

Hit the sack *later.* If you often lie awake, spending less time in bed than you typically sleep can help break that cycle, studies show. If you typically get 5 hours a night, set your alarm for that. Once you're sleeping for most of that time, go to bed 15 minutes earlier until you reach the recommended 8 hours a night.

Your Awesome 4somes

BREAKFAST

LUNCH

SNACK 1

DINNER

SNACK 2

Your DTOUR Workout
☐ Fat-Torch Walk (page 55), 25 minutes

> Remember: Success is nothing but luck.
> Just ask any failure.
> —AUTHOR UNKNOWN

HOW DID YOU DO?

BALANCE YOUR BLOOD SUGAR

	TIME	READING
CHECK 1		
CHECK 2		
CHECK 3		
CHECK 4		
CHECK 5		

SUCCEED ALL DAY

Push back breakfast. If you can't stomach an early-morning meal, eat it at 9:00, 10:00, or even 11:00 a.m. It will help you stay in control later in the day. **Launch a mite raid.** If nighttime coughing, sneezing, and snuffling disrupt your sleep and you don't have a cold, you could be allergic to dust mites. (Their residue can trigger mild to severe allergies.) To reduce allergens, vacuum and dust regularly. If you can, replace your mattress if it's more than 10 years old, and wash your pillow every week or put a miteproof plastic cover under your regular pillowcase. Crack the windows and doors, too. Increasing a room's airflow is one of the most effective ways to reduce mites.

DAY
12

Your Awesome 4somes

BREAKFAST

LUNCH

SNACK 1

DINNER

SNACK 2

Your DTOUR Workout
☐ Rest Day

> Your future depends on many things,
> but mostly on you.
> —FRANK TYGER

HOW DID YOU DO?

BALANCE YOUR BLOOD SUGAR

	TIME	READING
CHECK 1		
CHECK 2		
CHECK 3		
CHECK 4		
CHECK 5		

SUCCEED ALL DAY

Sign up for a race. It doesn't matter whether you're fast or slow, or even if you come in last. The idea is to set a goal. It gives you a tangible reason to put your sneakers on—you're in training. Making that commitment can be really motivating, because you'll want to do well on race day. Choose a race that's happening 8 to 10 weeks from today.

Rediscover the joy of cooking. Good nutrition helps short-circuit the effects of stress. If you're often too tired to cook after work, reframe the activity as a way to unwind rather than a chore. Shop over the weekend so you'll have everything you need. Pour a glass of wine, put on some smooth jazz, and hum as you chop, stir, and taste.

DAY
13

Your Awesome 4somes

BREAKFAST

LUNCH

SNACK 1

DINNER

SNACK 2

Your DTOUR Workout

☐ Metabo Moves (page 60)
☐ Belly Blast (page 65)

> ## Who dares, wins.
> —WINSTON CHURCHILL

HOW DID YOU DO?

BALANCE YOUR BLOOD SUGAR

	TIME	READING
CHECK 1		
CHECK 2		
CHECK 3		
CHECK 4		
CHECK 5		

SUCCEED ALL DAY

Nap cravings away. Fatigue can trigger food cravings. If you're tired at work, shut your office door, close your eyes, and reenergize. If you're at home, take a 15-minute catnap (but no longer than that).

Seek instant gratification. If you find it tough to wait for weeks to see the results of your efforts, fitness gadgets can provide right-now motivation. A heart rate monitor can tell you whether to increase or reduce the intensity of your workout, and a pedometer can boost your resolve to move more during the day.

Your Awesome 4somes

BREAKFAST

LUNCH

SNACK 1

DINNER

SNACK 2

Your DTOUR Workout

☐ Calorie-Scorch Walk (page 55), 20 minutes

Leap and the net will appear.
—JULIA CAMERON

HOW DID YOU DO?

BALANCE YOUR BLOOD SUGAR

	TIME	READING
CHECK 1		
CHECK 2		
CHECK 3		
CHECK 4		
CHECK 5		

MEASURE YOURSELF
Your weight: _____ pounds

SUCCEED ALL DAY
Set your alarm 15 minutes early. Those 900 extra seconds are a cushion against that inevitable morning chaos–making lunches, finding your car keys, arranging drop-offs and pickups for your kids.

Sip serenity now. The flower, vine, and leaves of the passionflower herb contain substances that have proven, gentle sedating qualities. Recommended by herbalists as a top treatment for insomnia, it's especially helpful when sleep is disturbed by anxiety. Use 1 teaspoon of dried herb per cup of boiling water.

DAY
15

Your Awesome 4somes

BREAKFAST

LUNCH

SNACK 1

DINNER

SNACK 2

Your DTOUR Workout
☐ Fat-Torch Walk (page 55), 30 minutes

> If you are in a hurry,
> you will never get there.
> —CHINESE PROVERB

HOW DID YOU DO?

BALANCE YOUR BLOOD SUGAR

	TIME	READING
CHECK 1		
CHECK 2		
CHECK 3		
CHECK 4		
CHECK 5		

SUCCEED ALL DAY

Instead of trying to ignore the craving, admit to it. This technique (cognitive diffusion) works on the same principle as getting the hots for a co-worker when you're happily partnered: Recognizing that you'll always be attracted to cute guys (or yummy foods) prevents you from acting on the feeling when it arises.

Prepare for the a.m. in the p.m. Make everyone's lunch for the next day the night before. Put out the clothes you plan to wear, and have your kids do it, too.

DAY
16

Your Awesome 4somes

BREAKFAST

LUNCH

SNACK 1

DINNER

SNACK 2

Your DTOUR Workout

☐ Calorie-Scorch Walk (page 55), 25 minutes

> The greater the obstacle,
> the more glory in overcoming it.
> —MOLIÈRE

HOW DID YOU DO?

BALANCE YOUR BLOOD SUGAR

	TIME	READING
CHECK 1		
CHECK 2		
CHECK 3		
CHECK 4		
CHECK 5		

SUCCEED ALL DAY

Hire a personal trainer for a workout or two. It's Day 16. Do you know where your motivation is? A few sessions with a pro can help ensure that you make it to the gym, perfect your technique, and boost your motivation.

Make breakfast your heaviest meal of the day. Digesting food takes energy, so if you eat a heavy meal late in the day, your body will be working hard to digest it when you're trying to go to sleep. Many people sleep better if they have protein at breakfast and lunch and then some carbohydrates at a light dinner.

DAY
17

Your Awesome 4somes

BREAKFAST

LUNCH

SNACK 1

DINNER

SNACK 2

Your DTOUR Workout

☐ Metabo Moves (page 60)
☐ Belly Blast (page 65)

> The harder you fall, the higher you bounce.
> —DOUG HORTON

HOW DID YOU DO?

BALANCE YOUR BLOOD SUGAR

	TIME	READING
CHECK 1		
CHECK 2		
CHECK 3		
CHECK 4		
CHECK 5		

SUCCEED ALL DAY

Feed a fantasy, starve a craving. Occupying your senses with a vivid nonfood fantasy can help stifle a craving, researchers at Flinders University in Australia found. Think about what some hot Hollywood actor looks like in nothing but a towel. You might forget all about those chips.

Go toward the light. Get outside when it's sunny, or at least turn on the lights at home in the morning. This will help you reset your awake-sleep cycle.

Your Awesome 4somes

BREAKFAST

LUNCH

SNACK 1

DINNER

SNACK 2

Your DTOUR Workout

☐ Fat-Torch Walk (page 55), 30 minutes

> Who has never tasted what is bitter
> does not know what is sweet.
> —GERMAN PROVERB

HOW DID YOU DO?

BALANCE YOUR BLOOD SUGAR

	TIME	READING
CHECK 1		
CHECK 2		
CHECK 3		
CHECK 4		
CHECK 5		

SUCCEED ALL DAY

Cut a high-energy soundtrack. Upbeat music makes a workout seem easier and go by faster, according to research conducted at the University of Scranton in Pennsylvania. That's because high-tempo music helps block out the sensations associated with pain and effort.

Got garden? Go dig. Researchers in the United Kingdom found that mice that inhaled bacteria commonly found in soil tried harder to solve a stressful problem (escaping from a pool of water); mice who didn't gave up more easily. The soil-loving bugs are thought to stimulate the release of mood-enhancing brain chemicals.

Your Awesome 4somes

BREAKFAST

LUNCH

SNACK 1

DINNER

SNACK 2

Your DTOUR Workout

☐ Rest Day

> One's best success comes after
> their greatest disappointments.
> —HENRY WARD BEECHER

HOW DID YOU DO?

BALANCE YOUR BLOOD SUGAR

	TIME	READING
CHECK 1		
CHECK 2		
CHECK 3		
CHECK 4		
CHECK 5		

SUCCEED ALL DAY

Forgo crash diets. It's common sense: The more restrictive your diet, the more likely you'll binge in rebellion. Consume a minimum of 1,200 calories a day, diet experts recommend.

If you splurge, get up—and active. Snarfing a pint of ice cream won't doom your weight loss if you don't let guilt derail your workout. In a French study, obese exercisers who bicycled for 45 minutes 3 hours after a high-fat meal metabolized more stored belly fat than those who cycled on an empty stomach. The upshot: All is not lost when you stray from your diet–in fact, your body may even kick it up a gear to help with damage control.

DAY
20

Your Awesome 4somes

BREAKFAST

LUNCH

SNACK 1

DINNER

SNACK 2

Your DTOUR Workout
☐ Calorie-Scorch Walk (page 55), 25 minutes

> Surround yourself with only people
> who are going to lift you higher.
> —OPRAH WINFREY

HOW DID YOU DO?

BALANCE YOUR BLOOD SUGAR

	TIME	READING
CHECK 1		
CHECK 2		
CHECK 3		
CHECK 4		
CHECK 5		

SUCCEED ALL DAY

Indulge in a before- or after-work "dogtail." For a few minutes before or after work, chase your pup around your backyard. He'll love the companionship and exercise. You'll love feeling like a 10-year-old again.

Cool out night sweats. If night sweats disrupt your sleep, keep your bedroom cool. A lower body temperature promotes sleep. Also, consider a low-dose oral contraceptive to even out hormone levels, especially if you also experience irregular menstrual cycles.

Your Awesome 4somes

BREAKFAST

LUNCH

SNACK 1

DINNER

SNACK 2

Your DTOUR Workout

☐ Metabo Moves (page 60)
☐ Belly Blast (page 65)

> There are no shortcuts
> to any place worth going.
> —BEVERLY SILLS

HOW DID YOU DO?

BALANCE YOUR BLOOD SUGAR

	TIME	READING
CHECK 1		
CHECK 2		
CHECK 3		
CHECK 4		
CHECK 5		

MEASURE YOURSELF

Your weight: _____ pounds

SUCCEED ALL DAY

Try an ex-smoker's craving buster. Suck a cinnamon stick or flavored toothpick, or chomp on sugarless gum.

Do unpleasant tasks first. Need to see your accountant? Get your teeth cleaned? Get the car inspected? Schedule any un-fun task for early in the day and get it over with. The rest of your day will be free of anxiety.

DAY
22

Your Awesome 4somes

BREAKFAST

LUNCH

SNACK 1

DINNER

SNACK 2

Your DTOUR Workout

☐ Fat-Torch Walk (page 55), 35 minutes

> Kites rise highest against the wind—
> not with it.
> —WINSTON CHURCHILL

HOW DID YOU DO?

BALANCE YOUR BLOOD SUGAR

	TIME	READING
CHECK 1		
CHECK 2		
CHECK 3		
CHECK 4		
CHECK 5		

SUCCEED ALL DAY

Take a picture. Slip into a swimsuit and take a photo. Place it somewhere where you'll see it constantly. Take a new photo every 4 weeks–and get stoked as your body transforms before your eyes.

Create a sleep schedule and stick to it. You may not be able to go to bed at the same time every night, but you can establish a regular wake-up time. Get up at the same time every morning, even on weekends.

Your Awesome 4somes

BREAKFAST

LUNCH

SNACK 1

DINNER

SNACK 2

Your DTOUR Workout

☐ Calorie-Scorch Walk (page 55), 30 minutes

> It is not because things are difficult
> that we do not dare, it is because we
> do not dare that they are difficult.
> —SENECA

HOW DID YOU DO?

BALANCE YOUR BLOOD SUGAR

	TIME	READING
CHECK 1		
CHECK 2		
CHECK 3		
CHECK 4		
CHECK 5		

SUCCEED ALL DAY

Make a reward list. List ways you can reward yourself for making it through another chocolate-chip-cookie craving. Buy yourself a new lipstick or rent a favorite video, for example.

Try magnesium. According to some naturopaths, this mineral helps make serotonin, which in turn produces melatonin, the brain chemical that sets your body clock and helps neurotransmitters (the ones that help us relax) work more efficiently. Take 200 to 300 mg of magnesium citrate daily with dinner. Because it works best when balanced with calcium (which aids absorption), also take 400 mg of calcium daily with lunch.

DAY
24

Your Awesome 4somes

BREAKFAST

LUNCH

SNACK 1

DINNER

SNACK 2

Your DTOUR Workout

☐ Metabo Moves (page 60)
☐ Belly Blast (page 65)

> Always bear in mind that your own resolution to succeed is more important than any one thing.
> —ABRAHAM LINCOLN

HOW DID YOU DO?

BALANCE YOUR BLOOD SUGAR

	TIME	READING
CHECK 1		
CHECK 2		
CHECK 3		
CHECK 4		
CHECK 5		

SUCCEED ALL DAY

Go on the defensive. If you need more inspiration to exercise than simply slimming down, consider a self-defense class. You'll learn a skill that can potentially save your life as you burn calories and build muscle.

Spot-check your posture. Stooping and slumping can lead to muscle tension and increased stress, so throughout the day, check your posture. Hold your head high and your spine and shoulders straight.

Your Awesome 4somes

BREAKFAST

LUNCH

SNACK 1

DINNER

SNACK 2

Your DTOUR Workout

☐ Rest Day

> The creation of a thousand forests
> is in one acorn.
> —RALPH WALDO EMERSON

HOW DID YOU DO?

BALANCE YOUR BLOOD SUGAR

	TIME	READING
CHECK 1		
CHECK 2		
CHECK 3		
CHECK 4		
CHECK 5		

SUCCEED ALL DAY

Stay hydrated. Drink at least eight 8-ounce glasses a day. Water is nature's appetite suppressant: It keeps your stomach full and prevents dehydration, which can lead to cravings and hunger.

Watch the rut. Every 4 to 6 weeks, switch up your workout routine (try a different walking route or new strength moves). You'll keep your motivation strong and your muscles challenged.

Your Awesome 4somes

BREAKFAST

LUNCH

SNACK 1

DINNER

SNACK 2

Your DTOUR Workout

☐ Fat-Torch Walk (page 55), 35 minutes

> Real difficulties can be overcome; it is only the imaginary ones that are unconquerable.
> —THEODORE N. VAIL

HOW DID YOU DO?

BALANCE YOUR BLOOD SUGAR

	TIME	READING
CHECK 1		
CHECK 2		
CHECK 3		
CHECK 4		
CHECK 5		

SUCCEED ALL DAY

Turn wait time into found time. Lines at the grocery store, bank, or post office are a fact of life. Plan for them. Tuck a paperback in your bag. Your "stressful" wait will turn into an oasis of calm.

De-stress with a good "book." Are you a worrier? Buy a small journal to use as a worry book. Choose a time during the day to regularly jot down concerns that keep you awake at night (anything from bills to world affairs). The idea is to worry *before* the lights go out—and to brainstorm potential solutions you can act on.

DAY
27

Your Awesome 4somes

BREAKFAST

LUNCH

SNACK 1

DINNER

SNACK 2

Your DTOUR Workout

☐ Calorie-Scorch Walk (page 55), 30 minutes

> Learn from yesterday, live for today,
> hope for tomorrow.
> —AUTHOR UNKNOWN

HOW DID YOU DO?

BALANCE YOUR BLOOD SUGAR

	TIME	READING
CHECK 1		
CHECK 2		
CHECK 3		
CHECK 4		
CHECK 5		

SUCCEED ALL DAY

Eat balanced meals. Eating meals that are very high in refined carbohydrates, such as pasta, can trigger cravings for more carbs and sugar. Balancing your meals with protein and a bit of healthy fat can dramatically reduce cravings.

Make three extra car and/or house keys. If you're constantly misplacing your keys, make a slew of spares. Carry a duplicate car key in your wallet. Hide a house key in a toolbox in the garage.

DAY
28

Your Awesome 4somes

BREAKFAST

LUNCH

SNACK 1

DINNER

SNACK 2

Your DTOUR Workout

☐ Metabo Moves (page 60)
☐ Belly Blast (page 65)

> # Do or do not. There is no try.
> ## —YODA

HOW DID YOU DO?

BALANCE YOUR BLOOD SUGAR

	TIME	READING
CHECK 1		
CHECK 2		
CHECK 3		
CHECK 4		
CHECK 5		

MEASURE YOURSELF

Your weight: _____ pounds

Your waistline: _____ inches

SUCCEED ALL DAY

Treat yourself. To celebrate your commitment to fitness, treat yourself to a little something at the end of each workout week: a new lipstick, a pedicure, a new skin-care product.

Calm down with chamomile. A bright, daisylike flower, chamomile has an age-old reputation for calming nerves and gently aiding sleep. Drinking 1 or 2 cups of tea before bedtime will help soothe you into sleep.

STAY ON THE ROAD TO SUCCESS

Whether you're at your goal weight or have a few more pounds to lose, continue to use the tools and techniques you've learned so far. We'll wager that you've gotten quite good at recognizing food sources of the Fat-Fighting 4 nutrients; gauging portion sizes; and timing your meals to prevent spikes and dips in your blood sugar. You're more aware of how physical activity, sleep, and stress management can ramp up weight loss and blood sugar control.

So keep up the good work! We're confident that you can do it. To help, we've put together a short to-do list of sorts—a collection of strategies that capture the key principles and guidelines of DTOUR. Review the list, memorize it, live by it. The payoff: long-term, lasting weight-loss success. (Remember, too, that you can always find insight, advice, and support at www.dtour.com.)

1. PICK YOUR CALORIE RANGE

You can continue using the DTOUR menus and recipes for as long as you'd like. We're sure you have your favorites! Feeling more adventurous? Then by all means expand your dietary horizons by creating your own meals. Just be sure to pay attention to your daily calorie intake.

◆ *To continue losing weight:* Stick with your current benchmark of 1,400 or 1,600 calories per day.

◆ *If you've reached your goal weight on the 1,400-calorie plan:* Increase to 1,600 calories a day and see how you fare. If you start to regain, cut back on calories—or burn more with exercise.

◆ *If you've reached your goal weight on the 1,600-calorie plan:* Add an extra 200-calorie snack every day. Men should aim for at least 1,700 calories per day once at their goal weight.

2. EAT EVERY 3 TO 4 HOURS

Eating at regular intervals is vital to keeping your blood sugar on an even keel. Did you notice a difference while eating this way over the past 6 weeks? If you're like our DTOUR panelists, you felt more energized, more focused, and less hungry. That's what optimal blood sugar control can do for you!

♦ *To continue losing weight:* Aim for three meals of approximately 350 to 400 calories each, plus two snacks of 175 to 200 calories each. (If you're eating 1,400 calories per day, you'll want to be at the lower end of these ranges; at 1,600 calories per day, you can go toward the higher end.)

♦ *If you've reached your goal weight and you want to maintain it:* Try for 400 calories at breakfast, lunch, and dinner, along with 200 calories at each snack. (Remember that you're adding a snack if you've been following the 1,600-calorie plan.)

3. STAY FAITHFUL TO THE FAT-FIGHTING 4

They've been your loyal allies for the past 6 weeks, helping you to whittle your waistline and balance your blood sugar. So why mess with a good thing? The Fat-Fighting 4 will continue to serve you well, provided you're getting enough of them. That means:

♦ At least 20 to 25 grams per day of fiber, both soluble and insoluble

♦ Two or 3 servings per day of low-fat dairy products fortified with vitamin D

♦ Between 2.5 and 2.7 grams per day of omega-3s from good sources such as fish (if you like it) or ground flaxseed or flaxseed oil, canola oil, or walnuts or walnut oil (if you don't)

4. SCORCH, TORCH, LIFT, AND SQUEEZE

Exercise isn't mandatory on DTOUR, but it definitely can enhance your results. You'll burn more calories not just during your workouts but all day long, as you build muscle and lose fat. You'll feel better, too—thanks in part to endorphins, those feel-good brain chemicals that contribute to a sense of well-being.

♦ *To continue losing weight:* Follow the DTOUR Workout as presented in the 4-Week Total Transformation, gradually stepping up the intensity and duration as you feel comfortable.

♦ *If you've reached your goal weight:* Your weekly exercise regimen should include at least one 30-minute Calorie-Scorch Walk, two 60-minute Fat-Torch Walks, and two sessions of the Metabo Moves and Belly Blast routines. Be sure to allow at least a day between strength-training sessions so your muscles have a chance to recover.

Your Awesome 4somes

BREAKFAST

LUNCH

SNACK 1

DINNER

SNACK 2

Your DTOUR Workout

☐ Fat-Torch Walk (page 55), 40 minutes

Improvement begins with I.
—ARNOLD H. GLASGOW

HOW DID YOU DO?

BALANCE YOUR BLOOD SUGAR

	TIME	READING
CHECK 1		
CHECK 2		
CHECK 3		
CHECK 4		
CHECK 5		

SUCCEED ALL DAY

Keep junk food out of the house. No matter how much your husband loves sticky buns or your kids love potato chips, if these foods aren't in your house, they won't be in your mouth. Tell your family they can buy, hide, and eat their treats in private.

Take a pre-bed bath. An hour and a half before bed, slip into a warm tub. The water will raise your body temperature, but it is the *drop* in body temperature that occurs when you get out that may leave you feeling sleepy.

DAY
30

Your Awesome 4somes

BREAKFAST

LUNCH

SNACK 1

DINNER

SNACK 2

Your DTOUR Workout

☐ Metabo Moves (page 60)
☐ Belly Blast (page 65)

> People become really quite remarkable when they start thinking that they can do things. When they believe in themselves they have the first secret of success.
> —NORMAN VINCENT PEALE

HOW DID YOU DO?

BALANCE YOUR BLOOD SUGAR

	TIME	READING
CHECK 1		
CHECK 2		
CHECK 3		
CHECK 4		
CHECK 5		

SUCCEED ALL DAY

Take a fitness adventure. Visit a rock-climbing wall. Go whitewater rafting. Such adventures double as workouts, and they can help you manage stress in everyday life, according to a study from Texas A&M University. **Shake up a stale routine.** Brush your teeth using the opposite hand. Rearrange your living room. Swap your crossword puzzle for Sudoku. Trying something new may ease your stress. Animal studies show that the brain rewards novelty by releasing the pleasure-inducing chemical dopamine.

Your Awesome 4somes

BREAKFAST

LUNCH

SNACK 1

DINNER

SNACK 2

Your DTOUR Workout

☐ Calorie-Scorch Walk (page 55), 35 minutes

> If you'll not settle for anything less than your best, you will be amazed at what you can accomplish in your lives.
> —VINCE LOMBARDI

HOW DID YOU DO?

BALANCE YOUR BLOOD SUGAR

	TIME	READING
CHECK 1		
CHECK 2		
CHECK 3		
CHECK 4		
CHECK 5		

SUCCEED ALL DAY

Engage your brain. When your mind is occupied with a Sudoku puzzle or a few rounds of computer solitaire, it's less likely to entertain thoughts of mint-chocolate-chip ice cream.

Give your senses a workout. Try that walking path by the river, or go to a nearby state park and walk in a sunny meadow, where you can smell the wild honeysuckle, tramp through freshly fallen snow, or count the bees and butterflies.

Your Awesome 4somes

BREAKFAST

LUNCH

SNACK 1

DINNER

SNACK 2

Your DTOUR Workout

☐ Rest Day

> Shoot for the moon.
> Even if you miss, you'll land among the stars.
> —LES BROWN

HOW DID YOU DO?

BALANCE YOUR BLOOD SUGAR

	TIME	READING
CHECK 1		
CHECK 2		
CHECK 3		
CHECK 4		
CHECK 5		

SUCCEED ALL DAY

Stay hydrated and prevent hunger. Is your throat parched? Did you skip breakfast *and* lunch? Both hunger and dehydration can set you on edge, aggravating feelings of tension and stress.

Finish your workout at least 3 hours before bed. In general, regular exercise makes it easier to fall asleep and improves sleep quality. However, working out within 3 hours of turning in is a bad idea. Rather than tiring you out, before-bed exercise makes you more alert—exactly what you don't need. Exercise also raises your body temperature (it can take as long as 6 hours for it to begin to drop again), and a cooler body temperature signals your brain that it is time to sleep.

Your Awesome 4somes

BREAKFAST

LUNCH

SNACK 1

DINNER

SNACK 2

Your DTOUR Workout

☐ Fat-Torch Walk (page 55), 40 minutes

> The men who try to do something
> and fail are infinitely better than those
> who try to do nothing and succeed.
> —LLOYD JONES

HOW DID YOU DO?

BALANCE YOUR BLOOD SUGAR

	TIME	READING
CHECK 1		
CHECK 2		
CHECK 3		
CHECK 4		
CHECK 5		

SUCCEED ALL DAY

Freeze! At the start or midway through a binge, stop in your tracks—perhaps with a cookie halfway to your mouth. This gives you the chance to come to your senses. If you've had 5 cookies but not the 6th, feel good that you stopped your binge cold.

Write down bits of good news each day. Every day, jot down five positive things that happened, suggests Carol Ryff, PhD, director of the Institute on Aging at the University of Wisconsin-Madison. To perceive your life as good, you need to focus on the gratifying things in it.

Your Awesome 4somes

BREAKFAST

LUNCH

SNACK 1

DINNER

SNACK 2

Your DTOUR Workout

☐ Metabo Moves (page 60)
☐ Belly Blast (page 65)

> Do not go where the path may lead, go
> instead where there is no path and leave a trail.
> —RALPH WALDO EMERSON

HOW DID YOU DO?

BALANCE YOUR BLOOD SUGAR

	TIME	READING
CHECK 1		
CHECK 2		
CHECK 3		
CHECK 4		
CHECK 5		

SUCCEED ALL DAY

Have a snack. The energy demands of exercise can lead your body to decide that you're overdoing it and slow down your metabolism. To prevent that, have a protein-and-healthy-carb snack–like a hard-boiled egg and a slice of whole wheat toast–2 hours before your workout.

Overhaul your meds. Medications used to treat cardiovascular or respiratory conditions can affect the neurotransmitters involved in sleep. Also, antihistamines and antidepressants can suppress REM sleep–the deep, recuperative stage tied to memory. Discuss these with your doctor. You may be able to switch drugs or change what time of day you take them.

DAY
35

Your Awesome 4somes

BREAKFAST

LUNCH

SNACK 1

DINNER

SNACK 2

Your DTOUR Workout

☐ Calorie-Scorch Walk (page 55), 35 minutes

> I am not discouraged, because every wrong attempt discarded is another step forward.
> —THOMAS A. EDISON

HOW DID YOU DO?

BALANCE YOUR BLOOD SUGAR

	TIME	READING
CHECK 1		
CHECK 2		
CHECK 3		
CHECK 4		
CHECK 5		

MEASURE YOURSELF

Your weight: _____ pounds

SUCCEED ALL DAY

Get back in the game. No matter what time of day a binge occurs, and no matter how dispirited it makes you feel, eat your next scheduled meal. If you binged at lunch, eat your normal dinner. It's a way to show yourself that you've begun to restore control.

Wind down with Dylan. A Taiwanese and American study of 60 troubled sleepers found that listening to soft music 45 minutes before bed for 3 weeks improved sleep quality and quantity by 35 percent. The key to finding a relaxing tune? Make sure it has 60 to 80 beats per minute, such as Bach preludes, Beethoven symphonies, or some folksy Bob Dylan.

Your Awesome 4somes

BREAKFAST

LUNCH

SNACK 1

DINNER

SNACK 2

Your DTOUR Workout

☐ Fat-Torch Walk (page 55), 40 minutes

> The future belongs to those who believe
> in the beauty of their dreams.
> —ELEANOR ROOSEVELT

HOW DID YOU DO?

BALANCE YOUR BLOOD SUGAR

	TIME	READING
CHECK 1		
CHECK 2		
CHECK 3		
CHECK 4		
CHECK 5		

SUCCEED ALL DAY

Invest in a heart rate monitor. A good one can cost $50 or more, but many people find it fun—and intensely motivating—to stay "in the zone."

Take a fresh look at stress. Jobs, relationships, long commutes, and credit card bills don't cause stress. It's our physical and mental reactions to these stimuli that can become problems. Accept that stress is a *reaction* to external factors, not the factors themselves, and you'll handle stress in a healthier way.

Your Awesome 4somes

BREAKFAST

LUNCH

SNACK 1

DINNER

SNACK 2

Your DTOUR Workout

☐ Metabo Moves (page 60)
☐ Belly Blast (page 65)

> Here is the test to find whether your mission on Earth is finished: If you're alive, it isn't.
> —RICHARD BACH

HOW DID YOU DO?

BALANCE YOUR BLOOD SUGAR

	TIME	READING
CHECK 1		
CHECK 2		
CHECK 3		
CHECK 4		
CHECK 5		

SUCCEED ALL DAY

Munch in front of the mirror. In the midst of a binge, eat your cookies or half-gallon of ice cream in front of the mirror. The sight of your reflection just might stop you cold.

Break a plateau. Has your weight loss slowed a bit? To bust through a plateau, try routinely varying the pace of your cardio. Exercisers who alternated between moderate- and high-intensity intervals burned nine times more fat than those who trained only at a moderate pace, a study at Laval University in Quebec found. When you strength train, change the number of reps you do and the weights you use.

DAY
38

Your Awesome 4somes

BREAKFAST

LUNCH

SNACK 1

DINNER

SNACK 2

Your DTOUR Workout

☐ Calorie-Scorch Walk (page 55), 35 minutes

> You can have anything you want
> if you are willing to give up the belief
> that you can't have it.
> —ROBERT ANTHONY

HOW DID YOU DO?

BALANCE YOUR BLOOD SUGAR

	TIME	READING
CHECK 1		
CHECK 2		
CHECK 3		
CHECK 4		
CHECK 5		

SUCCEED ALL DAY

Carry something calming. A photo of your child or family or a copy of a motivational quote or a verse from the Bible can act like a kind of visual mantra. When you're feeling stressed, take it out, gaze at it, and let it work its soothing magic.

Slip on some socks. The instant warmup dilates blood vessels in your feet, allowing your body to transfer heat from its core to the extremities, cooling you slightly, which induces sleep. Experts also suggest that an old-fashioned cloth nightcap achieves the same result (but consider its effect on your love life first).

Your Awesome 4somes

BREAKFAST

LUNCH

SNACK 1

DINNER

SNACK 2

Your DTOUR Workout

☐ Rest Day

> Nothing can stop the man with the right mental attitude from achieving his goal: Nothing on earth can help the man with the wrong mental attitude.
>
> —THOMAS JEFFERSON

HOW DID YOU DO?

BALANCE YOUR BLOOD SUGAR

	TIME	READING
CHECK 1		
CHECK 2		
CHECK 3		
CHECK 4		
CHECK 5		

SUCCEED ALL DAY

Give yourself a bright reminder. Stick a neon orange or green bandage on the index finger of your eating hand so you'll see it reaching for food. Once you notice your mindless munching, you can choose to stop it then and there.

Cultivate an attitude of gratitude. Deep down, most of us know how fortunate we are. So, once a day, say to yourself, "I'm fortunate to have _____ in my life," or "I'm grateful for _____." Fill in the blanks with the names of family and friends, or acknowledge your good health or a good job.

Your Awesome 4somes

BREAKFAST

LUNCH

SNACK 1

DINNER

SNACK 2

Your DTOUR Workout

☐ Fat-Torch Walk (page 55), 40 minutes

> In the confrontation between the stream and the rock, the stream always wins—not through strength, but through persistence.
> —BUDDHA

HOW DID YOU DO?

BALANCE YOUR BLOOD SUGAR

	TIME	READING
CHECK 1		
CHECK 2		
CHECK 3		
CHECK 4		
CHECK 5		

SUCCEED ALL DAY

Motivate step by step. Clip on a pedometer. Women who wear them typically walk 2,000 more steps a day than women who don't, according to researchers at Stanford University. They also lose more weight!

Talk yourself to sleep. After 8 weeks of cognitive-behavioral therapy, 33 insomniacs were able to alter negative thinking ("I'll never fall asleep") and develop better sleep habits, such as limiting time spent in bed to sleep and sex only. The therapy proved to be 30 percent more effective than insomnia drugs, reported Harvard Medical School and Beth Israel Deaconess Medical Center researchers in Boston.

Your Awesome 4somes

BREAKFAST

LUNCH

SNACK 1

DINNER

SNACK 2

Your DTOUR Workout

☐ Metabo Moves (page 60)
☐ Belly Blast (page 65)

> It takes as much stress to be
> a success as it does to be a failure.
> —EMILIO JAMES TRUJILLO

HOW DID YOU DO?

BALANCE YOUR BLOOD SUGAR

	TIME	READING
CHECK 1		
CHECK 2		
CHECK 3		
CHECK 4		
CHECK 5		

SUCCEED ALL DAY

Set a time limit. If you still crave a slice of pizza or a scoop of ice cream in an hour, you can have it. Most cravings don't last more than 10 minutes, so chances are that your craving will have vanished once the time's up.

Try a natural herbal aid. When insomnia results from anxiety, the herb kava promotes sleep by acting upon the brain's emotion centers and relaxing muscles, studies suggest. The recommended dose: one or two 400- to 500-milligram capsules an hour before bed.

Your Awesome 4somes

BREAKFAST

LUNCH

SNACK 1

DINNER

SNACK 2

Your DTOUR Workout

☐ Calorie-Scorch Walk (page 55), 35 minutes

> There are no secrets to success. It is the result of preparation, hard work, and learning from failure.
> —COLIN POWELL

HOW DID YOU DO?

BALANCE YOUR BLOOD SUGAR

	TIME	READING
CHECK 1		
CHECK 2		
CHECK 3		
CHECK 4		
CHECK 5		

MEASURE YOURSELF

Your weight: _____ pounds

SUCCEED ALL DAY

Join a local walking club. If you're longing for companionship on your route but can't find a walking buddy, look into joining an established club. You'll get a fresh route and some equally determined walking buddies.

Put off procrastination. What you want to do tomorrow, do today. What you want to do today, do now.

Your Awesome 4somes

BREAKFAST

LUNCH

SNACK 1

DINNER

SNACK 2

Your DTOUR Workout

☐ Fat-Torch Walk (page 55), 45 minutes

> You see things and say, "Why?"
> but I dream things and say, "Why not?"
> —GEORGE BERNARD SHAW

HOW DID YOU DO?

BALANCE YOUR BLOOD SUGAR

	TIME	READING
CHECK 1		
CHECK 2		
CHECK 3		
CHECK 4		
CHECK 5		

SUCCEED ALL DAY
Bust a binge with beats. Research has found that music activates the same feel-good center of the brain that eating your favorite foods does.

Play I Spy as you walk. Before you head out the door, decide what you'll count—squirrels, convertibles, slogans on T-shirts worn by passersby.

DAY
44

Your Awesome 4somes

BREAKFAST

LUNCH

SNACK 1

DINNER

SNACK 2

Your DTOUR Workout

- [ ] Metabo Moves (page 60)
- [ ] Belly Blast (page 65)

> Your body is your vehicle for life. As long as you are here, live in it. Love, honor, respect and cherish it, treat it well and it will serve you in kind.
> —SUZY PRUDDEN

HOW DID YOU DO?

BALANCE YOUR BLOOD SUGAR

	TIME	READING
CHECK 1		
CHECK 2		
CHECK 3		
CHECK 4		
CHECK 5		

SUCCEED ALL DAY

Take a nerve-soothing soak. Add chamomile, along with other calming herbs such as lavender and valerian, to bathwater. Wrap the dried herbs in some cheesecloth and hold it under the faucet while the tub fills.

Consider your pillow. If neck and shoulder aches keep you awake, try a down pillow. You want a pillow that is low enough to support your head without flexing your neck.

Your Awesome 4somes

BREAKFAST

LUNCH

SNACK 1

DINNER

SNACK 2

Your DTOUR Workout

☐ Calorie-Scorch Walk (page 55), 40 minutes

> Strength does not come from physical capacity. It comes from an indomitable will.
> —MAHATMA GANDHI

HOW DID YOU DO?

BALANCE YOUR BLOOD SUGAR

	TIME	READING
CHECK 1		
CHECK 2		
CHECK 3		
CHECK 4		
CHECK 5		

SUCCEED ALL DAY

Follow the "hands-full" rule when watching TV. TV and mindless munching go together like chips and dip. When you're parked in front of the tube, arm yourself with "hand busies"—a sewing or knitting project, a puzzle, your manicure kit and nails.

Try the relaxation response. Research shows that this simple technique short-circuits stress. Pick a focus word or phrase rooted in your personal belief system ("peace," for example). Sit quietly, close your eyes, and relax. Repeat your focus word each time you exhale. Continue for 10 to 20 minutes. Practice at least once a day.

Your Awesome 4somes

BREAKFAST

LUNCH

SNACK 1

DINNER

SNACK 2

Your DTOUR Workout

☐ Rest Day

> There is no man living who isn't capable of doing more than he thinks he can do.
>
> —HENRY FORD

HOW DID YOU DO?

BALANCE YOUR BLOOD SUGAR

	TIME	READING
CHECK 1		
CHECK 2		
CHECK 3		
CHECK 4		
CHECK 5		

SUCCEED ALL DAY

Walk the dog. Not only will you have a purpose for your outing, you'll have a companion as well. Don't have a dog? Borrow a neighbor's or a friend's.

Bore yourself to sleep. If you tend to fret when you hit the sheets, engage your brain with a tedious mental task. It's hard to worry about tomorrow when you're trying to count backward from 1,000 by 7s.

Your Awesome 4somes

BREAKFAST

LUNCH

SNACK 1

DINNER

SNACK 2

Your DTOUR Workout

☐ Fat-Torch Walk (page 55), 45 minutes

> Whether you think you can or whether you think you can't, you're right.
> —HENRY FORD

HOW DID YOU DO?

BALANCE YOUR BLOOD SUGAR

	TIME	READING
CHECK 1		
CHECK 2		
CHECK 3		
CHECK 4		
CHECK 5		

SUCCEED ALL DAY

Trick your sweet tooth with a whiff of vanilla. Experts theorize that the sweetness of vanilla sends neuropeptides (gut-to-brain messengers) into a kind of "sensory overload" that fools you into feeling like you've satisfied your sweet tooth. Vanilla scent from any source–an extract, a body lotion, or a candle–will do the trick.

Create a buffer time before bed. Soothing stories and lullabies prepare small children for sleep, right? Accord yourself the same treatment. Your version of a "bedtime story" might be a relaxing bubble bath or soothing music. Schedule it for an hour or so before turning in every night.

Your Awesome 4somes

BREAKFAST

LUNCH

SNACK 1

DINNER

SNACK 2

Your DTOUR Workout
☐ Metabo Moves (page 60)
☐ Belly Blast (page 65)

> If you do not hope, you will not find
> what is beyond your hopes.
> —ST. CLEMENT OF ALEXANDRIA

HOW DID YOU DO?

BALANCE YOUR BLOOD SUGAR

	TIME	READING
CHECK 1		
CHECK 2		
CHECK 3		
CHECK 4		
CHECK 5		

SUCCEED ALL DAY

Start a walking club. Can't find a local walking club? Ask neighbors and colleagues if they'd like to join you on a regular basis. Or, put up a "walkers wanted" ad on the bulletin board at your local supermarket, pharmacy, or natural-foods store.

Practice random acts of kindness every day. To shrug off your own stress, help strangers shed theirs. Give up your seat on the bus. Buy an extra latte to give to a co-worker. You'll find that the payback greatly exceeds the effort.

Your Awesome 4somes

BREAKFAST

LUNCH

SNACK 1

DINNER

SNACK 2

Your DTOUR Workout

☐ Calorie-Scorch Walk (page 55), 40 minutes

> I'm a great believer in luck, and I find the harder I work the more I have of it.
> —THOMAS JEFFERSON

HOW DID YOU DO?

BALANCE YOUR BLOOD SUGAR

	TIME	READING
CHECK 1		
CHECK 2		
CHECK 3		
CHECK 4		
CHECK 5		

MEASURE YOURSELF

Your weight: _____ pounds

SUCCEED ALL DAY

Avoid the food court at the mall. Sensory triggers (the smell of cinnamon buns) or visual cues (waitresses carrying hot fudge sundaes to happy customers) can set off cravings. If you can't avoid the food court, don sunglasses as you pass by, or take a hit off a mentholated inhaler.

Take your book club on the road. Hold your next book-club meeting on a local walking path. Walking at a brisk pace will still leave you with enough breath for a spirited discussion.

Your Awesome 4somes

BREAKFAST

LUNCH

SNACK 1

DINNER

SNACK 2

Your DTOUR Workout

☐ Fat-Torch Walk (page 55), 50 minutes

> You cannot discover oceans unless you
> have the courage to leave the shore.
> —AUTHOR UNKNOWN

HOW DID YOU DO?

BALANCE YOUR BLOOD SUGAR

	TIME	READING
CHECK 1		
CHECK 2		
CHECK 3		
CHECK 4		
CHECK 5		

SUCCEED ALL DAY

Stroll a labyrinth. Dating back thousands of years, these mazelike paths have beneficial effects on blood pressure and cortisol levels, research shows. It's relatively easy to find a labyrinth: More than 1,000 hospitals, schools, churches, and wellness centers in the United States have installed labyrinths. Search at wwll.veriditas.labyrinthsociety.org to find one near you.

Try some nighty-night nookie. If you need a reason, here's one: Some research suggests that hormonal mechanisms triggered during sex help enhance sleep. If sex makes you more stressed than sleepy, however, try another tip instead.

DAY
51

Your Awesome 4somes

BREAKFAST

LUNCH

SNACK 1

DINNER

SNACK 2

Your DTOUR Workout

- ☐ Metabo Moves (page 60)
- ☐ Belly Blast (page 65)

> The happiness of your life depends
> on the quality of your thoughts.
> —MARCUS AURELIUS

HOW DID YOU DO?

BALANCE YOUR BLOOD SUGAR

	TIME	READING
CHECK 1		
CHECK 2		
CHECK 3		
CHECK 4		
CHECK 5		

SUCCEED ALL DAY

Track your cravings. For a week, write down what you eat, how much, and at what time. This mini food journal can help you recognize craving and bingeing patterns. If you notice that you're prone to bingeing late at night, prepare a healthy snack and a diverting activity for that time.

"Downsize" twice a year. If clutter stresses you out, set aside a few hours every 6 months—perhaps in January and June—to go through your house, room by room. (You can even note the dates on your scheduling software, setting a reminder to be delivered the week before.) Decide what to keep, store, or give away.

Your Awesome 4somes

BREAKFAST

LUNCH

SNACK 1

DINNER

SNACK 2

Your DTOUR Workout

☐ Calorie-Scorch Walk (page 55), 45 minutes

> The golden opportunity you are seeking is in yourself. It is not in your environment; it is not in luck or chance, or the help of others; it is in yourself alone.
> —ORISON SWETT MARDEN

HOW DID YOU DO?

BALANCE YOUR BLOOD SUGAR

	TIME	READING
CHECK 1		
CHECK 2		
CHECK 3		
CHECK 4		
CHECK 5		

SUCCEED ALL DAY
Go on an inspiration safari. Where will you find it? In a magazine story, a song, a quotation? Search high and low, and don't stop until you find it.

Relax with a calming CD. Somna sleep-promoting audio CDs were developed by a sleep researcher. You can find them at http://somna.com.

DAY
53

Your Awesome 4somes

BREAKFAST

LUNCH

SNACK 1

DINNER

SNACK 2

Your DTOUR Workout

☐ Rest Day

> Success is the good fortune that comes from aspiration, desperation, perspiration, and inspiration.
> —EVAN ESAR

HOW DID YOU DO?

BALANCE YOUR BLOOD SUGAR

	TIME	READING
CHECK 1		
CHECK 2		
CHECK 3		
CHECK 4		
CHECK 5		

SUCCEED ALL DAY

Opt for quality, not quantity. Enjoy a small piece of dark chocolate instead of a whole bar of milk chocolate without doing lasting damage to your eating plan. The less you completely deny yourself, the more you are likely to crush a craving or head off a binge.

Tai chi yourself sleepy. Regular practice of tai chi chih, a Westernized version of the ancient Chinese martial art of tai chi, can help older adults with moderate sleep problems sleep better, a 2008 study at UCLA's David Geffen School of Medicine found.

Your Awesome 4somes

BREAKFAST

LUNCH

SNACK 1

DINNER

SNACK 2

Your DTOUR Workout

☐ Fat-Torch Walk (page 55), 50 minutes

> If you want the rainbow,
> you've got to put up with the rain.
> —JIMMY DURANTE

HOW DID YOU DO?

BALANCE YOUR BLOOD SUGAR

	TIME	READING
CHECK 1		
CHECK 2		
CHECK 3		
CHECK 4		
CHECK 5		

SUCCEED ALL DAY

Track your progress. Jot down your daily fitness achievements and compare them to your goals. When you see progress in black and white, your motivation will soar—and you'll attempt even more challenging goals.

Rediscover your hobbies. Before life got so crazy, what kinds of activities made you lose track of time? Think of creative ways to bring back those activities. You may have given up gardening because it throws your back out, but if you plant in pots set on a table at a comfortable height, you may be able to take joy in growing flowers or veggies once again.

DAY
55

Your Awesome 4somes

BREAKFAST

LUNCH

SNACK 1

DINNER

SNACK 2

Your DTOUR Workout

☐ Metabo Moves (page 60)
☐ Belly Blast (page 65)

There's no substitute for guts.
—PAUL "BEAR" BRYANT

HOW DID YOU DO?

BALANCE YOUR BLOOD SUGAR

	TIME	READING
CHECK 1		
CHECK 2		
CHECK 3		
CHECK 4		
CHECK 5		

SUCCEED ALL DAY
Invite your craving to make your day. If you're the rebellious type, try the defiant approach: "Go ahead, craving–take your best shot. I don't need chocolate-chip cookies and I'm not eating them!"

Walk for charity. Whether that walk for diabetes or a local animal shelter (or another close-to-your-heart cause) is scheduled for next month or next year, sign up now. You'll do good as you get in your walk. It's a win-win.

Your Awesome 4somes

BREAKFAST

LUNCH

SNACK 1

DINNER

SNACK 2

Your DTOUR Workout

☐ Calorie-Scorch Walk (page 55), 45 minutes

> If you don't risk anything,
> you risk even more.
> —ERICA JONG

HOW DID YOU DO?

BALANCE YOUR BLOOD SUGAR

	TIME	READING
CHECK 1		
CHECK 2		
CHECK 3		
CHECK 4		
CHECK 5		

MEASURE YOURSELF

Your weight: _____ pounds

Your waistline: _____ inches

SUCCEED ALL DAY

Create order out of chaos.
Organize your home and workspace so you always know exactly where things are. Put everything away where it belongs and you won't have the stress of searching for it.

Try affirmations. You might repeat "I let go of the day and enjoy peaceful sleep" several times as you prepare for bed.

DAY
57

Your Awesome 4somes

BREAKFAST

LUNCH

SNACK 1

DINNER

SNACK 2

Your DTOUR Workout

☐ Fat-Torch Walk (page 55), 55 minutes

> Every accomplishment begins
> with a decision to try.
> —EDWARD T. KELLY

HOW DID YOU DO?

BALANCE YOUR BLOOD SUGAR

	TIME	READING
CHECK 1		
CHECK 2		
CHECK 3		
CHECK 4		
CHECK 5		

SUCCEED ALL DAY

Sip a glass of vegetable juice before meals. Drinking vegetable juice before meals will help you eat 135 fewer calories at each meal, studies have shown.

Batch boring tasks. Putting off tasks you hate—cleaning your desk, answering e-mail, calling the cable and phone companies—creates stress. Solution: Do these tasks from hell one after the other. You'll get them done faster, because you'll be focused on getting them done faster.

Your Awesome 4somes

BREAKFAST

LUNCH

SNACK 1

DINNER

SNACK 2

Your DTOUR Workout

☐ Metabo Moves (page 60)
☐ Belly Blast (page 65)

> Being defeated is often a
> temporary condition. Giving up is
> what makes it permanent.
> —MARILYN VOS SAVANT

HOW DID YOU DO?

BALANCE YOUR BLOOD SUGAR

	TIME	READING
CHECK 1		
CHECK 2		
CHECK 3		
CHECK 4		
CHECK 5		

SUCCEED ALL DAY

Smile as you work out. Researchers have discovered that smiling even when you don't feel like it causes you to release more serotonin and endorphins, the brain's so-called happiness hormones.

Track your night's sleep. If it's 5 hours a night, set your alarm for that. Once you're sleeping most of that time, go to bed 15 minutes earlier until you reach the recommended 8 hours a night.

Your Awesome 4somes

BREAKFAST

LUNCH

SNACK 1

DINNER

SNACK 2

Your DTOUR Workout

☐ Calorie-Scorch Walk (page 55), 50 minutes

> You may have a fresh start any moment
> you choose, for this thing that we call failure
> is not the falling down, but the staying down.
> —MARY PICKFORD

HOW DID YOU DO?

BALANCE YOUR BLOOD SUGAR

	TIME	READING
CHECK 1		
CHECK 2		
CHECK 3		
CHECK 4		
CHECK 5		

SUCCEED ALL DAY

Back away from the salt shaker. Salt can worsen high blood pressure and add unwanted water weight to boot.

Sleep head north, feet south. As strange as it may sound, some alternative practitioners suggest that this position aligns your body with Earth's magnetic field, which brings your own energies into balance with the planet's. (If you try it, let us know how it worked for you.)

Your Awesome 4somes

BREAKFAST

LUNCH

SNACK 1

DINNER

SNACK 2

Your DTOUR Workout

☐ Rest Day

> There is a choice you have to make,
> in everything you do. And you must always
> keep in mind the choice you make, makes you.
> —AUTHOR UNKNOWN

HOW DID YOU DO?

BALANCE YOUR BLOOD SUGAR

	TIME	READING
CHECK 1		
CHECK 2		
CHECK 3		
CHECK 4		
CHECK 5		

SUCCEED ALL DAY

Imagine how you'll feel after a workout. Typically, you feel recharged, refreshed, raring to go, and proud. For 1 minute before you work out, close your eyes and let those positive emotions steep.

If you don't know, ask. Remember that episode of *Seinfeld* in which George Costanza, uncertain of whether he's been hired after a job interview, just starts showing up every day? Not knowing important information is stressful. Take a few moments to repeat someone's directions, expectations, and so forth after he or she tells you so you're sure you understand.

Your Awesome 4somes

BREAKFAST

LUNCH

SNACK 1

DINNER

SNACK 2

Your DTOUR Workout

☐ Fat-Torch Walk (page 55), 55 minutes

> You have to expect things of
> yourself before you can do them.
> —MICHAEL JORDAN

HOW DID YOU DO?

BALANCE YOUR BLOOD SUGAR

	TIME	READING
CHECK 1		
CHECK 2		
CHECK 3		
CHECK 4		
CHECK 5		

SUCCEED ALL DAY

Avoid your cravings for 2 weeks. After 5 days, the body yearns less for trigger foods, research shows—and after 2 weeks, the cravings are nearly gone.

Visualize a fitter you. You're sooo close to the end of the program! Keep up the good work—and before today's workout, close your eyes and, for 1 minute, picture yourself in your favorite swimsuit or skinny jeans. That mental picture is bound to spur you on.

DAY
62

Your Awesome 4somes

BREAKFAST

LUNCH

SNACK 1

DINNER

SNACK 2

Your DTOUR Workout

☐ Metabo Moves (page 60)
☐ Belly Blast (page 65)

> It takes courage to grow up
> and turn out to be who you really are.
> —E. E. CUMMINGS

HOW DID YOU DO?

BALANCE YOUR BLOOD SUGAR

	TIME	READING
CHECK 1		
CHECK 2		
CHECK 3		
CHECK 4		
CHECK 5		

SUCCEED ALL DAY

Blow off tension. This yogic breathing technique can help: Inhale deeply through your nose to a count of 8. Then, pucker your lips and exhale slowly through your mouth to a count of 15. Focus on the soft rush of your breath and feel the calm flood your body. Repeat 10 times.

Stand on golf balls. Strange? You bet. But according to reflexology experts, this helps "shock" the K1 meridian that runs along the bottoms of the feet. Interestingly, the K1 meridian is also known as the Chinese Sleep Point.

Your Awesome 4somes

BREAKFAST

LUNCH

SNACK 1

DINNER

SNACK 2

Your DTOUR Workout

☐ Calorie-Scorch Walk (page 55), 50 minutes

> In the long run, we shape our lives,
> and we shape ourselves. The process never
> ends until we die. And the choices we make
> are ultimately our responsibility.
> —ELEANOR ROOSEVELT

HOW DID YOU DO?

BALANCE YOUR BLOOD SUGAR

	TIME	READING
CHECK 1		
CHECK 2		
CHECK 3		
CHECK 4		
CHECK 5		

SUCCEED ALL DAY
Talk nicely to your craving. Thoughts like "I *must* have those chips" and "A bite won't hurt" escalate cravings. Swap them for positive thoughts such as "I ate more than I wanted to, but I'll stop now and get back on track" or "I am responsible for making smart decisions."

MEASURE YOURSELF
Your weight: _____ pounds

DAY
64

Your Awesome 4somes

BREAKFAST

LUNCH

SNACK 1

DINNER

SNACK 2

Your DTOUR Workout

☐ Fat-Torch Walk (page 55), 60 minutes

> Plan for the future, because that is where
> you are going to spend the rest of your life.
> —MARK TWAIN

HOW DID YOU DO?

BALANCE YOUR BLOOD SUGAR

	TIME	READING
CHECK 1		
CHECK 2		
CHECK 3		
CHECK 4		
CHECK 5		

SUCCEED ALL DAY

Read up on fitness. Treat yourself to a subscription to the fitness magazine that most inspires you. Bonus: You'll learn new tips and techniques that will keep your workouts fresh and fun.

Sleep the feng shui way. According to practitioners of this ancient Chinese art of creating environments that promote health and well-being, try not to have your bed directly under a window. This disturbs the energies around you and creates disharmony. Can't move your bed? Experts suggest covering the window with blinds and heavy curtains.